Juicing for Beginners

1200 Days of Fast and Tasty Recipes to Detoxify Your Body and Lose Weight

Natalie Orchard

© Copyright 2025 by Natalie Orchard - All rights reserved.

The following book is provided below with the aim of delivering information that is as precise and dependable as possible. However, purchasing this book implies an acknowledgment that both the publisher and the author are not experts in the discussed topics, and any recommendations or suggestions contained herein are solely for entertainment purposes. It is advised that professionals be consulted as needed before acting on any endorsed actions.

This statement is considered fair and valid by both the American Bar Association and the Committee of Publishers Association, and it holds legal binding throughout the United States.

Moreover, any transmission, duplication, or reproduction of this work, including specific information, will be deemed an illegal act, regardless of whether it is done electronically or in print. This includes creating secondary or tertiary copies of the work or recorded copies, which are only allowed with the express written consent from the Publisher. All additional rights are reserved.

The information in the following pages is generally considered to be a truthful and accurate account of facts. As such, any negligence, use, or misuse of the information by the reader will result in actions falling solely under their responsibility. There are no scenarios in which the publisher or the original author can be held liable for any difficulties or damages that may occur after undertaking the information described herein.

Additionally, the information in the following pages is intended solely for informational purposes and should be considered as such. As fitting its nature, it is presented without assurance regarding its prolonged validity or interim quality. Mention of trademarks is done without written consent and should not be construed as an endorsement from the trademark holder.

Table Of Contents

Chapter 1: Introduction to Juicing 9

   The Journey Begins: Embracing a Healthier Lifestyle 9

   Understanding Juicing: Benefits and Basics 11

   Setting Realistic Goals and Expectations......................................13

Chapter 2: Juicing Essentials 17

   Selecting the Right Equipment: Juicers and Accessories.........................17

   The Best Ingredients for Maximum Health Benefits................................20

   Storing and Preserving Fresh Juices..24

Chapter 3: The Science of Juicing 29

   Nutritional Breakdown: What Goes into Your Juice? 29

   Debunking Myths: Separating Fact from Fiction 31

   Juicing for Specific Health Goals: Weight Loss, Detox, and More............34

Chapter 4: Detoxifying Juices... 37

   Green Detox Delights 37

      Kale and Cucumber Cleanse 37

      Spinach Ginger Detox 38

      Broccoli Citrus Boost...38

      Sweet Beet Detoxifier 38

   Citrus Cleansers 39

      Sunrise Citrus Zinger 39

      Minty Lemonade Cleanse...39

      Ginger Citrus Blast 39

      Tropical Citrus Twist...40

   Herbal Infusions for Cleansing 40

      Soothing Peppermint Elixir 40

      Dandelion Detox Brew 40

      Ginger Tulsi Tonic...41

      Calming Chamomile Concoction 41

Chapter 5: Weight Loss Juices... 43

   Fat-Burning Fruit Blends 43

      Berry Metabolism-Booster.......................................43

      Citrus Fat-Cutter 44

      Pineapple Green Slimmer 44

      Apple Cinnamon Burn 44

   Low-Calorie Vegetable Mixes 45

Cucumber Celery Hydrator 45

Spicy Tomato Twist 45

Zesty Carrot Ginger 45

Beetroot and Spinach Slim 46

Metabolism-Boosting Combinations 46

Green Tea Citrus Fusion 46

Spicy Ginger Zest 46

Cinnamon Apple Booster.. 46

Minty Watermelon Cooler 47

Chapter 6: Energy-Boosting Juices 49

Morning Kickstarters 49

Sunrise Ginger Spark... 49

Avocado & Spinach Power Smoothie 50

Beetroot Citrus Booster 50

Green Tea Apple Zest... 50

Midday Energy Elixirs 51

Tropical Turmeric Reviver.. 51

Green Energy Boost 51

Citrus Beet Booster 51

Berry Almond Bliss 52

Pre-Workout Power Juices 52

Apple Beet Performance Enhancer 52

Citrus Kick Juice 52

Pineapple Spinach Power Smoothie.. 53

Matcha Energy Booster 53

Chapter 7: Immunity-Boosting Juices 55

Vitamin-Packed Recipes 55

Kiwi Kale Vitamin Booster 55

Carrot-Orange Immunity Mix 56

Recipe 3: Berry Blast Antioxidant Shake 56

Green Tea Citrus Fusion 56

Antioxidant-Rich Blends.. 57

Pomegranate Blueberry Bliss 57

Acai Antioxidant Power 57

Green Matcha Mixer 57

Cherry Almond Antioxidant Shake 58

Cold and Flu Fighters 58

Ginger Lemonade Soother.. 58

    Turmeric Pineapple Immunity Boost 58

    Berry Echinacea Elixir 59

    Spicy Citrus Defense..................................59

Chapter 8: Digestive Health Juices 61

  Soothing Digestive Aids..................................61

    Minty Fennel Digestive Soother..................................61

    Papaya Ginger Calmer 62

    Cucumber Aloe Cooler 62

    Apple Celery Digestive Aid 62

  Fiber-Rich Juices 63

    Apple-Pear Fiber Booster..................................63

    Berry Chia Digestive Mix 63

    Carrot-Ginger Fiber Fix 63

    Spinach Avocado Fiber Blend 64

  Gut-Healthy Probiotic Mixes..................................64

    Kefir Kale Smoothie 64

    Probiotic Berry Blast 64

    Apple-Cinnamon Probiotic Drink 64

    Mango Lassi Probiotic Smoothie 65

Chapter 9: Heart-Healthy Juices..................... 67

  Cholesterol-Lowering Recipes..................................67

    Oatmeal Almond Smoothie..................................67

    Red Berry Flaxseed Juice 68

    Green Tea Citrus Infusion 68

    Avocado Spinach Smoothie..................................68

  Blood Pressure Balancers 69

    Celery Cucumber Cooler 69

    Beetroot Ginger Blast 69

    Pomegranate Parsley Power..................................69

    Spinach Kiwi Kalm 69

  Heart-Protective Blends 70

    Walnut Blueberry Bliss 70

    Omega Orange Medley..................................70

    Avocado Apple Affair 71

    Kale Kiwi Kardia 71

Chapter 10: Skin and Beauty Juices 73

  Radiant Skin Recipes..................................73

Cucumber Mint Refresher 73

Carrot Ginger Glow 74

Berry Basil Bliss 74

Avocado Citrus Cream 74

Anti-Aging Juices 75

Pomegranate Blueberry Potion 75

Golden Turmeric Elixir 75

Avocado Green Smoothie 75

Red Radiance Booster 75

Hair and Nail Strengthening Mixes 76

Silky Strawberry Almond Bliss 76

Cucumber Spinach Rejuvenator 76

Carrot Avocado Power Drink 77

Walnut Berry Fusion 77

Chapter 11: Mind and Mood Enhancing Juices 79

Stress-Relieving Sips 79

Lavender Lemonade Zen 79

Chamomile Apple Elixir 80

Minty Green Relaxer 80

Berry Basil Bliss 80

Mood-Boosting Mixtures 81

Sunshine Citrus Smoothie 81

Berry Bliss Booster 81

Green Mood Lifter 81

Tropical Happiness Juice 82

Brain-Boosting Beverages 82

Blueberry Brainwave Smoothie 82

Avocado & Walnut Elixir 82

Matcha Memory Booster 83

Ginger-Citrus Brain Buzz 83

Chapter 12: Specialized Juices for Unique Needs 85

Juices for Athletes and Fitness Enthusiasts 85

Energizing Beetroot Blast 85

Spinach Power Potion 86

Citrus Endurance Enhancer 86

Banana-Strawberry Protein Smoothie 86

Juices for Seniors and Children 87

Gentle Apple Carrot Delight 87

Berry Banana Bliss 87

Tropical Digestive Aid 87

Soothing Peach Oat Smoothie...87

Seasonal and Exotic Juice Recipes..88

Dragon Fruit Sunrise..88

Pomegranate Persimmon Potion 88

Starfruit Citrus Splash..88

Lychee Lavender Elixir 89

Chapter 13: Conclusion and Moving Forward 91

Reflecting on Your Juicing Journey 91

Incorporating Juicing into Your Daily Routine 92

Continuing Your Path to Wellness 94

Chapter 1: Introduction to Juicing

The Journey Begins: Embracing a Healthier Lifestyle

In the early light of dawn, the world seems to pause, holding its breath in those precious moments before the day begins. It's a time of reflection, of considering the choices we make and the paths we tread. For many of us, this reflection often centers on our health and well-being. We find ourselves asking, "How can I live a healthier, more fulfilling life?" The answer, as you will discover in this journey, often lies in the simple yet profound act of juicing.

Juicing is not just a culinary practice; it's a gateway to a healthier lifestyle. It's a commitment to nourishing your body with the purest essence of nature's bounty. This chapter marks the beginning of a transformative journey where you'll learn not only the hows but also the whys of juicing. It's about understanding the power of natural, nutrient-rich diets and how they can enhance not just your own health, but the well-being of your entire family.

The Art of Juicing: A Symphony of Flavors and Nutrients

Imagine walking into a market, the air rich with the scent of fresh produce. You're surrounded by vibrant colors - the deep greens of kale and spinach, the fiery reds of bell peppers, the sunny yellows of lemons. These are not just ingredients; they are the building blocks of your health.

Juicing is an art, one that allows you to blend these diverse elements into a symphony of flavors and nutrients. Each ingredient you choose serves a purpose, whether it's the cleansing power of celery or the antioxidant richness of blueberries. As you embark on this journey, you'll learn how to create concoctions that not only taste delightful but also provide your body with essential vitamins, minerals, and enzymes.

But juicing is more than just combining flavors; it's about understanding the benefits each juice offers. Whether it's a green juice to kickstart your morning or a beetroot blend to fuel your workout, each glass is a step towards holistic nutrition. You will learn to craft juices that align with your body's needs and your family's health goals, transforming your kitchen into a haven of wellness.

Beyond the Glass: Nourishing Lives Through Juicing

As you delve deeper into the world of juicing, you'll find it's about more than just what's in your glass; it's about what each sip represents. It's a commitment to choosing natural over processed, fresh over artificial. It's about taking control of your health and that of your family, ensuring that each meal is a testament to the love and care you pour into it.

This chapter is more than an introduction to juicing; it's an invitation to a new way of life. It's about empowering yourself with the knowledge to make informed choices about your diet. You'll learn to navigate through the overwhelming world of nutrition and find clarity in the simplicity of juicing. It's about taking the first step in a journey that promises vitality, wellness, and a deeper connection with the food you consume.

As you turn each page, you'll find stories of individuals who have transformed their lives through juicing, practical tips to incorporate juicing into your busy schedule, and insights into how to make juicing a joyful and sustainable part of your lifestyle. This journey is not just about discovering new recipes; it's about uncovering a new perspective on health and well-being.

A New Chapter in Health

As we conclude this introductory chapter, remember that every journey begins with a single step. The path to a healthier lifestyle through juicing is not just a series of recipes; it's a tapestry woven with the threads of nutrition, wellness, and mindfulness. It's a commitment to yourself and your loved ones, a promise to nurture and nourish.

Embrace this journey with an open heart and a curious mind. Let each page inspire you, each recipe invigorates you, and each story empower you. Welcome to the world of juicing, where every sip is a step towards a healthier, happier you.

Understanding Juicing: Benefits and Basics

Juicing, at its core, is an alchemy of sorts – a vibrant fusion of nature's freshest produce transformed into a liquid elixir teeming with life and vitality. It's a process that extracts the pure essence of fruits and vegetables, concentrating their nutrients, flavors, and benefits into a form that's both enjoyable and highly absorbable by the body. For anyone embarking on a journey toward a more health-conscious life, understanding the basics and benefits of juicing is an essential first step.

In a world where fast food and processed meals often take center stage, juicing stands out as a beacon of wellness, offering a straightforward and effective way to incorporate more fruits and vegetables into our diets. It's not just about quenching thirst or seeking a quick health fix; it's about embracing a lifestyle that prioritizes the nourishment of our bodies and minds.

Nutritional Powerhouses: Unleashing the Benefits

When we talk about the benefits of juicing, we're delving into a realm where every sip is a step toward better health. Juices are nutritional powerhouses, packed with vitamins, minerals, antioxidants, and enzymes that are crucial for bodily function and optimal health. They offer a concentrated source of these nutrients in a readily digestible form, making it easier for the body to absorb and utilize them.

Juicing allows for a diverse intake of fruits and vegetables – more than one might typically consume in a day. This variety is key to obtaining a wide spectrum of nutrients, each with its unique role in maintaining health. For instance, the vitamin C in citrus fruits boosts immunity, while the potassium in leafy greens supports heart health. The antioxidants in berries combat oxidative stress, and the enzymes in fresh pineapple aid digestion.

But the benefits of juicing go beyond just the physical. There's a psychological aspect to it as well. Preparing and consuming fresh juices can be a meditative, mindful practice – a moment in your day to focus on self-care and the choices you make towards a healthier lifestyle. This mindfulness can lead to better dietary choices overall, creating a positive feedback loop of wellness.

Juicing as a Catalyst for Change

Embarking on a juicing journey can be transformative. It's not uncommon for individuals to report increased energy levels, improved digestion, clearer skin, and even a greater sense of overall well-being after incorporating juicing into their routine. For women seeking to enhance their family's health and educate others on the benefits of holistic nutrition, juicing can be a powerful tool.

Juicing introduces simplicity and purity into our diets – a welcome change from the complexity and ambiguity that often surrounds modern eating habits. It teaches us to appreciate the natural flavors and textures of fruits and vegetables, and it encourages us to make conscious choices about what we put into our bodies.

Moreover, juicing can be a stepping stone to exploring broader aspects of nutrition and wellness. As you learn about the various ingredients and their benefits, you begin to develop a deeper understanding of holistic health. This knowledge is empowering, allowing you to make informed decisions that can positively impact your family's health and the health of your clients.

A Foundation for Wellness

As this chapter on the benefits and basics of juicing concludes, remember that this is just the beginning. Juicing is more than a dietary addition; it's a foundation for a lifetime of wellness. It's an invitation to explore, experiment, and experience the myriad ways in which nature's bounty can nourish and revitalize us.

Whether you're a seasoned juicer or a curious newcomer, let this journey be one of discovery and delight. Let each juice you create be a celebration of health, a testament to the power of simple, natural ingredients. Welcome to the world of juicing, where each glass is not just a drink, but a step towards a healthier, happier life.

Setting Realistic Goals and Expectations

Embarking on a journey of juicing is not just about adding new recipes to your diet; it's about embracing a lifestyle change. As with any significant change, it's crucial to approach juicing with realistic goals and expectations. Setting clear, achievable objectives can be the difference between a fleeting interest and a lasting, impactful transformation in your health and well-being.

For many, the allure of juicing comes with the promise of quick health fixes - rapid weight loss, instant energy boosts, or miraculous healing. While juicing certainly offers a plethora of health benefits, it's important to ground these expectations in reality. Juicing should be seen as a complement to a balanced diet and healthy lifestyle, not a panacea.

Crafting Your Juicing Goals: Personalization is Key

Your journey with juicing should be as unique as you are. This means setting goals that align with your personal health needs, lifestyle, and tastes. For some, the primary goal may be to increase the intake of fruits and vegetables; for others, it could be about exploring natural ways to boost energy or enhance skin health.

When setting these goals, consider the practical aspects. How can juicing fit into your daily routine? What changes are you prepared to make? For those leading busy lives, it might mean starting with a simple morning juice routine. For others, it could involve experimenting with different ingredients to address specific health concerns.

As you set these goals, remember to be patient with yourself. Change takes time, and the benefits of juicing, while profound, don't occur overnight. It's about gradual improvement and consistency. Celebrate the small victories - whether it's feeling more energized, noticing a glow in your skin, or simply enjoying the process of making fresh juice.

Managing Expectations: The Balanced View

It's equally important to manage expectations. Juicing, like any dietary change, can have varied effects on the body. While many experiences positive outcomes, it's vital to listen to your body and adjust accordingly. Not every juice recipe will suit everyone, and it's okay to tweak recipes to suit your taste and health needs.

Understanding that juicing is a journey of discovery can help manage expectations. It's a process of learning what works best for your body and adjusting your juicing habits to optimize health benefits. Be open to trying new combinations and exploring different ingredients. However, also be aware that some juices may not agree with you, and that's a natural part of the process.

In the context of holistic health, it's also important to note that juicing is not a substitute for whole fruits and vegetables. While juicing extracts vitamins, minerals, and antioxidants, it often leaves behind fiber. Therefore, it should be part of a balanced diet that includes a variety of whole foods.

A Journey of Health and Self-Discovery

As this chapter concludes, reflect on the idea that setting realistic goals and expectations in juicing is more than just a step in a dietary change – it's a step towards a deeper understanding of your health and well-being. Juicing is a journey that encourages you to connect with your body's needs, explore new flavors, and embrace a healthier lifestyle.

This journey is not just about what you consume; it's about cultivating awareness, understanding your body, and making mindful choices that enhance your overall well-being. As you continue this journey, let your goals and expectations evolve with you, guiding you towards a healthier, more vibrant life.

Chapter 2: Juicing Essentials

Selecting the Right Equipment: Juicers and Accessories

At the heart of every juicing journey is the juicer itself, a tool that transforms raw fruits and vegetables into a vibrant liquid full of health benefits. Selecting the right juicer is a pivotal decision that can influence your juicing experience, efficiency, and the quality of your juice. There are several types of juicers available, each with its unique features and benefits.

Centrifugal juicers are popular for their speed and convenience. They work by using a fast-spinning metal blade that separates juice from flesh via centrifugal force.

These are great for beginners due to their ease of use and quick juicing capabilities. However, they may not be as efficient in extracting juice from leafy greens like kale or spinach.

Masticating juicers, also known as cold-press juicers, operate at slower speeds and use a gear (auger) to crush the produce. They are excellent at extracting juice from virtually all types of fruits and vegetables, including leafy greens and wheatgrass. Masticating juicers are known for producing higher yields and retaining more nutrients due to less heat and oxidation.

Triturating juicers, also known as twin-gear juicers, use two interlocking gears to crush and press produce. They are highly efficient, providing the highest yield and nutrient retention. These are ideal for the serious juicer who is willing to invest more time and money into their juicing practice.

Choosing the right juicer will depend on your lifestyle, budget, and what you plan to juice most often. Each type has its pros and cons, and the best choice is the one that aligns with your juicing goals and preferences.

Enhancing Your Juicing Experience: Must-Have Accessories

While the juicer is the star of the show, accessories can greatly enhance your juicing experience. A few well-chosen tools can make the process of juicing more efficient, enjoyable, and even expand the variety of juices you can create.

A good quality knife and cutting board are essential for prepping your fruits and vegetables. A sharp knife will make the chopping process quicker and more precise, while a sturdy cutting board will provide a safe and stable surface.

Strainers and sieves are useful for those who prefer pulp-free juice. They can also be used to make nut milks or to strain herbal infusions for added variety in your juice repertoire.

Glass storage containers or mason jars are ideal for storing juice. They preserve the freshness and prevent contamination. If you plan to juice in batches, having a set of these containers will be invaluable.

A produce brush is essential for cleaning your fruits and vegetables, especially if you're using organic produce. Proper cleaning ensures that your juices are free from dirt and other residues.

Measuring cups and spoons can be helpful for following recipes accurately, especially when you are starting out or experimenting with new ingredients and combinations.

Juicing with Ease: Maintenance and Care

Maintaining your juicer is critical to its longevity and performance. Each type of juicer has its specific cleaning requirements, but there are some general practices that apply to all.

Clean your juicer immediately after use. Allowing pulp and juice residue to dry makes it harder to clean and can lead to bacterial growth.

Use the brushes provided or a soft brush to clean the nooks and crannies where pulp can get trapped. For parts that are dishwasher-safe, regular cleaning in the dishwasher can ensure thorough sanitation.

Regularly check the blades or augers for dullness or damage. Sharp components are essential for efficient juicing and the safety of the appliance.

Lubricate moving parts as recommended by the manufacturer. This can help prevent wear and tear, especially in masticating and triturating juicers.

Your Gateway to Healthful Juicing

Investing in the right equipment and accessories is the first step in ensuring a successful and enjoyable juicing journey. By choosing a juicer that suits your needs, complementing it with the right accessories, and maintaining it well, you set the stage for a fulfilling and health-enhancing juicing experience.

Remember, the tools you choose are your allies in achieving your health goals. They are the foundation upon which your juicing habits will build and flourish. As you continue on this path, let your equipment be a reflection of your commitment to health, wellness, and the joys of juicing.

The Best Ingredients for Maximum Health Benefits

In the alchemy of juicing, ingredients play the starring role. Each fruit, vegetable, and herb bring its unique profile of nutrients, flavors, and health benefits. Selecting the right ingredients is not just about taste—it's about maximizing the health benefits of each juice you create. This section delves into the world of produce, highlighting the best ingredients for a healthful juicing journey.

Fruits: The Sweet Powerhouses

Fruits are nature's sweets, packed with vitamins, minerals, and antioxidants. They are essential in juicing for their flavor and nutrient content. Here are some fruits that offer exceptional health benefits:

- **Apples**: High in fiber and vitamin C, apples are perfect for adding a natural sweetness to any juice. They also aid in digestion and can help regulate blood sugar levels.
- **Berries**: Blueberries, strawberries, and raspberries are rich in antioxidants, which protect your cells from damage. They are also high in fiber and vitamins.
- **Citrus Fruits**: Oranges, lemons, and grapefruits are full of vitamin C, which boosts the immune system. They also add a refreshing zing to your juices.
- **Pineapple**: Contains bromelain, an enzyme that aids in digestion and has anti-inflammatory properties.

Vegetables: The Nutrient-Dense Heroes

Vegetables are the cornerstone of nutritious juicing. They provide essential vitamins and minerals with fewer calories and sugar than fruits.

- **Leafy Greens**: Kale, spinach, and Swiss chard are rich in iron, calcium, and vitamins A, C, and K. They are also high in chlorophyll, which detoxifies the blood.
- **Beets**: High in folate, manganese, and nitrates, beets improve blood flow and blood pressure.
- **Carrots**: Known for their high beta-carotene content, which converts to vitamin A in the body, carrots are great for skin and eye health.
- **Celery**: A natural diuretic, celery supports kidney function and contains anti-inflammatory compounds.

To elevate the nutritional profile of your juices, consider adding superfoods and herbs. These ingredients pack a potent punch of nutrients and health benefits in small quantities.

Superfoods

- **Spirulina**: A blue-green algae, spirulina is a complete protein and is rich in B-vitamins and minerals.
- **Chia Seeds**: High in omega-3 fatty acids, fiber, and protein, chia seeds can be soaked and added to juices for a nutrient boost.
- **Ginger**: Known for its digestive and anti-inflammatory properties, ginger adds a spicy kick to juices.
- **Turmeric**: Contains curcumin, a compound with powerful anti-inflammatory and antioxidant properties.

Herbs

- **Mint**: Adds a refreshing flavor and aids in digestion.
- **Parsley**: Rich in vitamins A, C, and K, parsley also supports kidney health and detoxification.
- **Cilantro**: Known for its heavy metal detoxifying properties, cilantro also adds a unique flavor to juices.

Embracing Variety for Holistic Health

The key to maximizing the health benefits of juicing is variety. Different fruits and vegetables offer different nutrients and health benefits. By rotating your ingredients regularly, you ensure your body receives a broad spectrum of nutrients. This not only contributes to your physical health but also keeps your juicing routine exciting and flavorful.

Seasonal and Local: The Freshness Factor

Wherever possible, choose seasonal and locally grown produce. Seasonal fruits and vegetables are picked at their peak of freshness, ensuring the highest nutrient content and best flavor. Local produce also tends to be fresher as it doesn't undergo long transport and storage periods.

Crafting Your Health Elixir

In the art of juicing, your ingredients are your colors, and your glass is the canvas. Each ingredient you choose brings its unique hue of health benefits, creating a mosaic of wellness in every glass. By selecting the best ingredients – balancing fruits, vegetables, superfoods, and herbs – you craft not just a beverage, but a health elixir that nourishes your body, delights your palate, and rejuvenates your soul. As you continue your juicing journey, let each ingredient be a choice towards a healthier, more vibrant you.

Storing and Preserving Fresh Juices

Juicing is an art that extends beyond the creation of a nutritious drink; it encompasses the preservation of its vitality and nutrients. The process of storing and preserving fresh juices is crucial in maintaining their health benefits and flavor. Freshly made juices are devoid of the preservatives found in commercial products, making them susceptible to rapid nutrient degradation and spoilage. Understanding the basics of storage and preservation is key to ensuring each glass of juice remains as beneficial and delicious as when it was first made.

The Role of Oxygen and Light

Exposure to air and light are the primary culprits in diminishing the quality of fresh juice. Oxygen can lead to oxidation, a process that degrades nutrients and alters the taste and color of the juice. Light, especially sunlight, can have a similar effect, breaking down sensitive vitamins and enzymes. Storing juices in airtight containers and keeping them away from direct light helps to minimize these effects.

Best Practices for Juice Storage

Once the juice is made, its journey to your glass should be swift to retain its nutritional prowess. Here are some best practices for storing your fresh juices:

Choosing the Right Containers

Glass Over Plastic: Glass containers are preferred for juice storage as they do not leach chemicals and can be sealed tightly. Mason jars are a popular, readily available option.

Size Matters: Use containers that are the right size for your juice servings. Less air in the container means less oxidation.

Seal Tightly: Ensure the lids of your containers are airtight. Oxygen absorbers or vacuum sealers can be used for an extra layer of protection.

Temperature is Key

Refrigeration: Fresh juices should be stored in the refrigerator immediately after juicing. The cold temperature slows down the degradation process.

Freezing: For longer storage, freezing is an option. While it might slightly alter the texture and taste, freezing preserves most of the nutrients. Use freezer-safe containers and leave some room at the top as liquids expand when frozen.

The Shelf Life of Fresh Juices

The shelf life of fresh juice depends on various factors including the type of juicer used, the ingredients, and the storage method. Generally, juices from centrifugal juicers should be consumed immediately, while those from masticating or triturating juicers can be stored for up to 24-48 hours. Always check the juice for any signs of spoilage, like off smell or taste, before consuming.

Rotation and Consumption

First In, First Out: Rotate your juices in the fridge, so you consume the older ones first.

Labeling: Label your containers with the juicing date to keep track of their freshness.

Advanced Preservation Techniques

For those looking to extend the shelf life further, there are advanced preservation techniques:

Vacuum Sealing: Removes air from the container, slowing oxidation.

High-Pressure Processing (HPP): Though more complex and less accessible for home juicers, HPP is a method used commercially to extend shelf life without heating and thus retaining nutrients.

Savoring Every Sip with Proper Storage

The journey of a juice from ingredients to glass is a testament to your commitment to health. Proper storage and preservation practices are the final, crucial steps in this journey. By understanding and implementing these practices, you ensure that each sip of your fresh juice is as nourishing and flavorful as possible.

In the world of juicing, where freshness and nutrition are paramount, mastering the art of storage is as essential as the juicing process itself. As you continue to explore and enjoy the myriad benefits of juicing, let the care you put into storing your creations be a reflection of your dedication to a healthier, more vibrant life.

Chapter 3: The Science of Juicing

Nutritional Breakdown: What Goes into Your Juice?

Juicing is not just a culinary activity; it's a scientific endeavor that transforms whole fruits and vegetables into a nutrient-packed beverage. Each ingredient in your juice plays a distinct role, contributing vitamins, minerals, enzymes, and phytonutrients essential for health. This section delves into the nutritional essence of juicing, unveiling the complex symphony of nutrients present in every sip.

Vitamins and Minerals: The Essentials

Juices are teeming with vitamins and minerals, the essential micronutrients that play key roles in maintaining bodily functions. Here's a glimpse into some of these vital nutrients:

- **Vitamins such as A, C, and E**: Found abundantly in fruits and vegetables, these vitamins are crucial for immune function, skin health, and protecting the body against oxidative stress.
- **B Vitamins**: Present in leafy greens and some fruits, they are vital for energy metabolism and nervous system health.
- **Minerals like potassium, magnesium, and calcium**: These are pivotal for heart health, bone strength, and muscle function.

Enzymes: Nature's Catalysts

Fresh, raw juices are rich in natural enzymes. These biological catalysts aid in digestion and help break down food to release its full nutritional potential. Unlike cooked or processed foods, which lose these precious enzymes, fresh juices deliver them intact, supporting your body's digestive and metabolic processes.

Phytonutrients: The Hidden Gems

Phytonutrients, or plant compounds, are what give fruits and vegetables their vibrant colors and unique flavors. They have potent health-promoting properties:

- **Flavonoids and Carotenoids**: Known for their antioxidant properties, they help combat inflammation and reduce the risk of chronic diseases.
- **Chlorophyll**: Found in green vegetables, it's known for its detoxifying properties.
- **Phytoestrogens**: Found in certain fruits and vegetables, they can help balance hormones in the body.

The Impact of Juicing on Nutrient Absorption

Juicing offers a unique benefit – it breaks down plant cell walls, making it easier for the body to absorb and assimilate these nutrients. This means that the vitamins, minerals, and phytonutrients are more readily available for your body's use than they would be from eating whole fruits and vegetables, especially for those with digestive challenges.

Maximizing Nutrient Intake

- **Combining Ingredients Wisely**: Understanding which ingredients complement each other not only creates a delicious juice but also optimizes nutrient absorption. For example, pairing vitamin C rich fruits with iron-rich greens can enhance iron absorption.
- **Diversifying Your Juices**: Regularly rotating the fruits and vegetables you juice ensures a broader spectrum of nutrients and minimizes exposure to any single type of pesticide or contaminant.

The Role of Fiber in Juicing

One important aspect to consider in the science of juicing is fiber. While juicing removes most of the fiber found in whole fruits and vegetables, the nutrients that are concentrated in the juice are more easily absorbed. However, it's important to maintain a balanced diet that includes whole fruits and vegetables for adequate fiber intake.

The Balance of Juicing and Whole Foods

- **Incorporating Whole Foods**: To ensure a well-rounded diet, complement your juicing regimen with whole fruits and vegetables, whole grains, lean proteins, and healthy fats.
- **Understanding Your Body's Needs**: Each person's dietary requirements are unique. Listen to your body and adjust your juicing habits to suit your individual health needs and goals.

A Deep Dive into Nutritional Alchemy

Juicing is more than just a trendy health practice; it's a science-backed approach to consuming concentrated forms of vital nutrients. By understanding the nutritional breakdown of your juices, you can tailor your juicing practices to better meet your health goals, be it boosting immunity, enhancing digestion, or simply maintaining overall wellness. In this chapter, we've peeled back the layers to reveal the intricate tapestry of nutrients that make up each glass of juice. As you continue your juicing journey, let this knowledge guide you in making informed choices, leading to a healthier, more vibrant life.

Debunking Myths: Separating Fact from Fiction

Juicing, with its rising popularity, has become a subject of various myths and misconceptions. These myths range from overblown claims of miraculous health benefits to undue criticisms that overlook the genuine advantages of juicing. In this section, we will navigate through some common myths, separating fact from fiction and providing a clearer understanding of what juicing can and cannot do for you.

Myth 1: Juicing is a Complete Meal Replacement

- **Reality Check**: While fresh juices are rich in vitamins and minerals, they lack essential nutrients like protein and healthy fats. Juices should complement a balanced diet, not replace whole meals. The key is to integrate juicing as a part of a varied and nutritious diet.

Myth 2: Juicing Detoxifies the Body

- **Scientific Perspective**: The human body is equipped with its own efficient detoxification system, including the liver, kidneys, and intestines. While certain juices can support these organs' function, they do not 'detoxify' the body in a medical sense. Nutrient-rich juices can aid in maintaining overall health, which in turn supports the body's natural detox processes.

Understanding Juicing and Weight Loss

One of the most prevalent myths about juicing is its role in weight loss. Let's explore this aspect with a factual lens.

Myth 3: Juicing is a Quick Fix for Weight Loss

- **The Balanced View**: Juicing can be part of a weight loss strategy, primarily because it can help increase your intake of fruits and vegetables. However, sustainable weight loss involves a comprehensive lifestyle change encompassing a balanced diet and regular physical activity. Juicing alone, without other dietary and lifestyle modifications, is not a magic solution for weight loss.

The Truth About Nutrients in Juicing

Misconceptions about the nutritional value of juices need to be addressed for a better understanding of what goes into your glass.

Myth 4: Juicing Destroys All the Nutrients

- **Fact Over Fiction**: While it's true that the process of juicing can lead to some nutrient loss, particularly in terms of fiber, it does not destroy all the nutrients. In fact, juicing can make certain nutrients more readily available for absorption. The key is in the method of juicing and the freshness of the produce.

Myth 5: Packaged Juices are as Good as Freshly Made Juices

- **Understanding the Difference**: Packaged juices, even those labeled as 'natural' or 'pure', often undergo processes like pasteurization and may contain preservatives and added sugars. These processes can significantly reduce the nutrient content. Freshly made juices, on the other hand, maintain their nutritional integrity.

Juicing and Blood Sugar Management

The impact of juicing on blood sugar levels is often a topic of concern, especially for individuals with diabetes or insulin resistance.

Myth 6: Juicing Always Leads to High Blood Sugar Spikes

- **Nuanced Understanding**: While fruit juices can cause a more rapid increase in blood sugar compared to whole fruits, not all juices have the same effect. The key is to focus on vegetable-based juices, limit the fruit content, and include ingredients that are lower on the glycemic index. Additionally, consuming juices as part of a meal can help mitigate blood sugar spikes.

Embracing Juicing with Informed Understanding

Debunking these myths is crucial in embracing juicing as part of a healthy lifestyle. Juicing, when done right and integrated sensibly into your diet, can provide a host of benefits. It's an excellent way to supplement your diet with additional vitamins, minerals, and phytonutrients.

The key is to approach juicing with a balanced perspective, understanding its role within a broader nutritional context. As you continue your journey in the world of juicing, let knowledge and fact-based understanding guide your choices, enabling you to reap the maximum benefits that juicing has to offer.

Juicing for Specific Health Goals: Weight Loss, Detox, and More

Juicing, when tailored to specific health goals, can be a powerful tool in your wellness arsenal. This section explores how to optimize your juicing regimen for various objectives, such as weight loss, detoxification, and enhancing overall health.

Juicing for Weight Loss: Beyond Calorie Counting

- **Strategic Ingredient Selection**: For weight loss, the focus should be on vegetables rather than fruits, particularly those that are lower in sugar like cucumbers, celery, and leafy greens. These ingredients provide essential nutrients without excessive calories.
- **Balancing with Protein and Fiber**: While juices lack protein and fiber, integrating them with a balanced diet that includes these macronutrients can help manage hunger and maintain muscle mass during weight loss.
- **The Role of Hydration**: Juicing also contributes to hydration, which is essential for metabolism and can help with appetite control.

Detoxifying Your Body: The Natural Way

- **Supporting Natural Detoxification**: While the body is naturally equipped to detoxify itself, certain juices can support this process. Ingredients like beets, lemon, and ginger are known to support liver health, a key organ in detoxification.
- **Antioxidant-Rich Juices**: Green juices, rich in antioxidants, can aid in neutralizing free radicals, thereby supporting the body's natural cleansing processes.

Juicing for Enhanced Wellness

Nutrient-Dense Juices for Overall Health

- **Boosting Immunity**: Juices rich in vitamin C, such as those containing citrus fruits and leafy greens, can strengthen the immune system.

- **Improving Digestive Health**: Ingredients like aloe vera, cucumber, and fennel have soothing properties for the digestive system. Additionally, including fruits like pineapple and papaya, which contain digestive enzymes, can aid in digestion.

Targeted Juices for Specific Needs

- **Juices for Energy**: Ingredients like beets, which enhance blood flow, and apples, which provide natural sugars, can be excellent for boosting energy.
- **Heart Health**: Juices with ingredients high in potassium and antioxidants, such as berries and leafy greens, support cardiovascular health.
- **Skin and Beauty**: Cucumber, carrot, and citrus fruits, known for their skin-hydrating and -nourishing properties, can be great additions to juices for skin health.

The Mindful Approach to Juicing

Understanding Limitations and Complementing Diet

- **Complementary, not a Substitute**: Juicing should be viewed as a complement to a balanced diet, not a replacement for whole foods. Whole fruits and vegetables provide fiber and other nutrients that are essential for health.

Chapter 4: Detoxifying Juices

Green Detox Delights

Kale and Cucumber Cleanse

- **Preparation Time:** 10 minutes
- **Ingredients:** 1 cup kale leaves, 1 large cucumber, 1 green apple, half a lemon (juiced), 1-inch ginger root
- **Servings:** 2
- **Preparation Method:** Juicing

- **Procedure:** 1. Wash all ingredients thoroughly. 2. Cut the cucumber and apple into manageable pieces. 3. Start juicing the kale leaves, followed by cucumber, apple, and ginger. 4. Finally, add the lemon juice into the mix.
- **Nutritional Values (per serving):** Calories: 95 kcal, Protein: 2g, Carbohydrates: 22g, Fat: 0.6g, Fiber: 4g, Sugars: 12g

Spinach Ginger Detox

- **Preparation Time:** 8 minutes
- **Ingredients:** 2 cups fresh spinach, 1 pear, 1 tablespoon chopped ginger, 1 tablespoon fresh mint leaves, 1 celery stalk
- **Servings:** 1
- **Preparation Method:** Juicing
- **Procedure:** 1. Clean all produce and chop into small pieces. 2. Juice the spinach, pear, and celery together. 3. Add ginger and mint for a final spin in the juicer. 4. Stir and serve immediately.
- **Nutritional Values (per serving):** Calories: 120 kcal, Protein: 1.5g, Carbohydrates: 29g, Fat: 0.5g, Fiber: 5g, Sugars: 20g

Broccoli Citrus Boost

- **Preparation Time:** 12 minutes
- **Ingredients:** 1 cup broccoli florets, 2 carrots, 1 orange (peeled), 1/2 lime (juiced), 1/2 cup parsley
- **Servings:** 2
- **Preparation Method:** Juicing
- **Procedure:** 1. Rinse broccoli, carrots, parsley, and orange. 2. Chop carrots and orange for easier juicing. 3. Juice all ingredients, starting with the softer ones like orange and finishing with broccoli. 4. Squeeze in lime juice and stir.
- **Nutritional Values (per serving):** Calories: 85 kcal, Protein: 3g, Carbohydrates: 19g, Fat: 0.3g, Fiber: 6g, Sugars: 9g

Sweet Beet Detoxifier

- **Preparation Time:** 15 minutes
- **Ingredients:** 1 medium beetroot, 1 red apple, 1 carrot, 1-inch turmeric root, 1/2 lemon (juiced)
- **Servings:** 2
- **Preparation Method:** Juicing
- **Procedure:** 1. Thoroughly wash all ingredients. 2. Peel and chop the beetroot, apple, and carrot. 3. Juice all the ingredients together, starting with the softer ones. 4. Add the lemon juice and give a final stir.
- **Nutritional Values (per serving):** Calories: 110 kcal, Protein: 2g, Carbohydrates: 26g, Fat: 0.4g, Fiber: 5g, Sugars: 18g

Citrus Cleansers

Sunrise Citrus Zinger

- **Preparation Time:** 7 minutes
- **Ingredients:** 2 oranges, peeled; 1 grapefruit, peeled; 1/2 lemon, peeled; 1-inch piece of turmeric root
- **Servings:** 1
- **Preparation Method:** Juicing
- **Procedure:** 1. Thoroughly wash all fruits and turmeric. 2. Cut fruits into segments that fit your juicer. 3. Juice all the ingredients, starting with the citrus fruits and ending with turmeric. 4. Stir the juice well before serving.
- **Nutritional Values (per serving):** Calories: 180 kcal, Protein: 3g, Carbohydrates: 45g, Fat: 0.5g, Fiber: 8g, Sugars: 35g

Minty Lemonade Cleanse

- **Preparation Time:** 5 minutes
- **Ingredients:** 3 lemons, peeled; 1 lime, peeled; 1/4 cup fresh mint leaves; 1 tablespoon honey (optional)
- **Servings:** 2
- **Preparation Method:** Juicing
- **Procedure:** 1. Rinse lemons, lime, and mint leaves. 2. Juice the lemons and lime first. 3. Add mint leaves to the juicer last. 4. Mix in honey if desired, and serve chilled.
- **Nutritional Values (per serving):** Calories: 60 kcal, Protein: 1g, Carbohydrates: 20g, Fat: 0g, Fiber: 2g, Sugars: 6g (excluding honey)

Ginger Citrus Blast

- **Preparation Time:** 10 minutes
- **Ingredients:** 1 orange, peeled; 1/2 grapefruit, peeled; 1/2 lemon, peeled; 1-inch ginger root; 1 carrot
- **Servings:** 1
- **Preparation Method:** Juicing
- **Procedure:** 1. Wash all ingredients and peel where necessary. 2. Chop ingredients into sizes suitable for your juicer. 3. Begin juicing with the carrot, followed by ginger, and then the citrus fruits. 4. Stir well and serve immediately.
- **Nutritional Values (per serving):** Calories: 120 kcal, Protein: 2g, Carbohydrates: 30g, Fat: 0.3g, Fiber: 6g, Sugars: 22g

Tropical Citrus Twist

- **Preparation Time:** 8 minutes
- **Ingredients:** 2 tangerines, peeled; 1/2 lime, peeled; 1/2 lemon, peeled; 1/2 cup pineapple chunks; small handful of cilantros
- **Servings:** 2
- **Preparation Method:** Juicing
- **Procedure:** 1. Rinse tangerines, lime, lemon, pineapple, and cilantro. 2. Juice the citrus fruits first, followed by pineapple and cilantro. 3. Stir thoroughly and serve over ice.
- **Nutritional Values (per serving):** Calories: 70 kcal, Protein: 1g, Carbohydrates: 18g, Fat: 0.2g, Fiber: 3g, Sugars: 14g

---

Herbal Infusions for Cleansing

Soothing Peppermint Elixir

- **Preparation Time:** 5 minutes
- **Ingredients:** 1/4 cup fresh peppermint leaves, 1 tablespoon honey, 1 lemon, juiced, 2 cups hot water
- **Servings:** 2
- **Preparation Method:** Infusion
- **Procedure:** 1. Rinse peppermint leaves and add them to a heatproof container. 2. Pour hot water over the leaves. 3. Steep for 3-4 minutes. 4. Stir in fresh lemon juice and honey. 5. Strain and serve.
- **Nutritional Values (per serving):** Calories: 50 kcal, Protein: 0.3g, Carbohydrates: 13g, Fat: 0g, Fiber: 0.5g, Sugars: 12g

Dandelion Detox Brew

- **Preparation Time:** 10 minutes
- **Ingredients:** 2 tablespoons dried dandelion leaves, 1 teaspoon grated ginger, 2 cups boiling water, 1 teaspoon lemon zest
- **Servings:** 2
- **Preparation Method:** Infusion
- **Procedure:** 1. Combine dandelion leaves, ginger, and lemon zest in a pot. 2. Add boiling water and cover. 3. Steep for 7-8 minutes. 4. Strain and serve warm.
- **Nutritional Values (per serving):** Calories: 5 kcal, Protein: 0.1g, Carbohydrates: 1g, Fat: 0g, Fiber: 0.2g, Sugars: 0g

Ginger Tulsi Tonic

- **Preparation Time:** 8 minutes
- **Ingredients:** 1/4 cup tulsi (holy basil) leaves, 2 inches fresh ginger root, sliced, 2 cups water, 1 tablespoon honey
- **Servings:** 2
- **Preparation Method:** Infusion
- **Procedure:** 1. Add tulsi leaves and sliced ginger to a teapot. 2. Boil water and pour over the leaves and ginger. 3. Let it steep for 5-6 minutes. 4. Sweeten with honey before serving.
- **Nutritional Values (per serving):** Calories: 45 kcal, Protein: 0.2g, Carbohydrates: 11g, Fat: 0g, Fiber: 0.1g, Sugars: 10g

- **Nutritional Values (per serving):** Calories: 35 kcal, Protein: 0g, Carbohydrates: 9g, Fat: 0g, Fiber: 0g, Sugars: 8g

Calming Chamomile Concoction

- **Preparation Time:** 5 minutes
- **Ingredients:** 2 tablespoons dried chamomile flowers, 2 cups hot water, 1 teaspoon raw honey, a few drops of lemon juice
- **Servings:** 2
- **Preparation Method:** Infusion
- **Procedure:** 1. Place chamomile flowers in a teapot or infuser. 2. Add hot water and let steep for 4 minutes. 3. Add honey and lemon juice to taste. 4. Strain into cups and serve.

Chapter 5: Weight Loss Juices

Fat-Burning Fruit Blends

Berry Metabolism-Booster

- **Preparation Time:** 5 minutes
- **Ingredients:** 1/2 cup blueberries, 1/2 cup strawberries, 1/4 cup raspberries, 1/2 lemon, juiced, 1/2 cup cold water
- **Servings:** 1
- **Preparation Method:** Blending

- **Procedure:** 1. Wash all berries and add them to a blender. 2. Squeeze the lemon juice into the blender. 3. Add cold water for a smoother consistency. 4. Blend until smooth. 5. Serve immediately.
- **Nutritional Values (per serving):** Calories: 70 kcal, Protein: 1g, Carbohydrates: 17g, Fat: 0.5g, Fiber: 4g, Sugars: 11g

Citrus Fat-Cutter

- **Preparation Time:** 6 minutes
- **Ingredients:** 1 grapefruit, peeled and seeded, 1 orange, peeled, 1 teaspoon grated ginger, 1/2 cup sparkling water
- **Servings:** 2
- **Preparation Method:** Blending
- **Procedure:** 1. Segment the grapefruit and orange and place in a blender. 2. Add grated ginger. 3. Blend until smooth. 4. Stir in sparkling water for a refreshing twist. 5. Serve chilled.
- **Nutritional Values (per serving):** Calories: 80 kcal, Protein: 1.5g, Carbohydrates: 20g, Fat: 0.2g, Fiber: 3g, Sugars: 16g

Pineapple Green Slimmer

- **Preparation Time:** 7 minutes
- **Ingredients:** 1 cup fresh pineapple chunks, 1/2 cucumber, 1/2 lime, juiced, 1/4 cup fresh mint leaves, 1/2 cup water
- **Servings:** 1
- **Preparation Method:** Blending
- **Procedure:** 1. Combine pineapple, cucumber, and mint leaves in a blender. 2. Squeeze in the lime juice. 3. Add water for desired consistency. 4. Blend until smooth. 5. Enjoy this refreshing mix.

- **Nutritional Values (per serving):** Calories: 100 kcal, Protein: 1g, Carbohydrates: 25g, Fat: 0.3g, Fiber: 3g, Sugars: 18g

Apple Cinnamon Burn

- **Preparation Time:** 8 minutes
- **Ingredients:** 1 apple, cored and sliced, 1/2 teaspoon ground cinnamon, 1/2 teaspoon honey, 1 cup almond milk
- **Servings:** 1
- **Preparation Method:** Blending
- **Procedure:** 1. Place apple slices in a blender. 2. Add cinnamon and honey. 3. Pour in almond milk for a creamy texture. 4. Blend until smooth and well combined. 5. Serve this spiced delight immediately.
- **Nutritional Values (per serving):** Calories: 95 kcal, Protein: 1g, Carbohydrates: 21g, Fat: 2.5g, Fiber: 4g, Sugars: 15g

Low-Calorie Vegetable Mixes

Cucumber Celery Hydrator

- **Preparation Time:** 10 minutes
- **Ingredients:** 1 large cucumber, 3 celery stalks, 1/4 cup parsley, 1 green apple, 1/2 lemon, juiced
- **Servings:** 2
- **Preparation Method:** Juicing
- **Procedure:** 1. Wash and chop cucumber, celery, and apple. 2. Juice cucumber, celery, and apple. 3. Add parsley to the juicer. 4. Stir in fresh lemon juice. 5. Serve immediately.
- **Nutritional Values (per serving):** Calories: 60 kcal, Protein: 1.5g, Carbohydrates: 14g, Fat: 0.2g, Fiber: 3g, Sugars: 10g

Spicy Tomato Twist

- **Preparation Time:** 8 minutes
- **Ingredients:** 2 large tomatoes, 1/2 red bell pepper, 1/4 teaspoon cayenne pepper, 1/2 teaspoon sea salt, 1 cup water
- **Servings:** 2
- **Preparation Method:** Blending
- **Procedure:** 1. Cut tomatoes and red bell pepper into chunks. 2. Blend tomatoes and red bell pepper with water. 3. Add cayenne pepper and sea salt. 4. Blend until smooth. 5. Serve chilled.
- **Nutritional Values (per serving):** Calories: 35 kcal, Protein: 1.6g, Carbohydrates: 8g, Fat: 0.2g, Fiber: 2g, Sugars: 6g

Zesty Carrot Ginger

- **Preparation Time:** 7 minutes
- **Ingredients:** 3 carrots, 1-inch ginger root, 1/2 lemon, juiced, 1 cup water
- **Servings:** 1
- **Preparation Method:** Juicing
- **Procedure:** 1. Peel and chop carrots and ginger. 2. Juice carrots and ginger together. 3. Add lemon juice. 4. Mix well and serve.
- **Nutritional Values (per serving):** Calories: 70 kcal, Protein: 1g, Carbohydrates: 16g, Fat: 0.3g, Fiber: 4g, Sugars: 9g

Beetroot and Spinach Slim

- **Preparation Time:** 12 minutes
- **Ingredients:** 1 small beetroot, 2 cups spinach, 1/2 cucumber, 1/2 lemon, juiced, 1/2 cup water
- **Servings:** 2
- **Preparation Method:** Juicing
- **Procedure:** 1. Chop beetroot and cucumber. 2. Juice beetroot, spinach, and cucumber. 3. Add lemon juice and water. 4. Stir well and serve chilled.
- **Nutritional Values (per serving):** Calories: 50 kcal, Protein: 2g, Carbohydrates: 11g, Fat: 0.2g, Fiber: 3g, Sugars: 7g

Metabolism-Boosting Combinations

Green Tea Citrus Fusion

- **Preparation Time:** 15 minutes
- **Ingredients:** 1 green tea bag, 1/2 grapefruit, 1/4 lemon, 1 teaspoon honey, 2 cups hot water
- **Servings:** 2
- **Preparation Method:** Infusion
- **Procedure:** 1. Steep the green tea bag in hot water for 5 minutes. 2. Squeeze the juice from the grapefruit and lemon into the tea. 3. Stir in honey for sweetness. 4. Allow to cool and serve over ice.
- **Nutritional Values (per serving):** Calories: 30 kcal, Protein: 0.5g, Carbohydrates: 7g, Fat: 0g, Fiber: 1g, Sugars: 6g

Spicy Ginger Zest

- **Preparation Time:** 10 minutes
- **Ingredients:** 1-inch ginger root, 1 cucumber, 1/2 apple, 1/4 teaspoon cayenne pepper, 2 cups water
- **Servings:** 1
- **Preparation Method:** Juicing
- **Procedure:** 1. Peel and chop ginger. 2. Juice ginger with cucumber and apple. 3. Add cayenne pepper to the juice and stir well. 4. Serve chilled for a refreshing taste.
- **Nutritional Values (per serving):** Calories: 60 kcal, Protein: 1g, Carbohydrates: 14g, Fat: 0.2g, Fiber: 3g, Sugars: 10g

Cinnamon Apple Booster

- **Preparation Time:** 5 minutes

- **Ingredients:** 2 apples, 1/2 teaspoon ground cinnamon, 1 cup cold water, 1/2 teaspoon honey (optional)
- **Servings:** 2
- **Preparation Method:** Blending
- **Procedure:** 1. Core and slice apples. 2. Blend apples with water and cinnamon until smooth. 3. Add honey for extra sweetness if desired. 4. Serve immediately for a crisp and energizing drink.
- **Nutritional Values (per serving):** Calories: 55 kcal, Protein: 0.5g, Carbohydrates: 14g, Fat: 0.2g, Fiber: 2.5g, Sugars: 11g

Minty Watermelon Cooler

- **Preparation Time:** 8 minutes
- **Ingredients:** 2 cups cubed watermelon, 1/4 cup fresh mint leaves, 1/2 lime, juiced, 1 cup ice water
- **Servings:** 2
- **Preparation Method:** Blending
- **Procedure:** 1. Combine watermelon, mint leaves, and lime juice in a blender. 2. Add ice water for a refreshing twist. 3. Blend until smooth. 4. Serve immediately for a hydrating and metabolism-boosting refreshment.
- **Nutritional Values (per serving):** Calories: 40 kcal, Protein: 1g, Carbohydrates: 10g, Fat: 0.2g, Fiber: 1g, Sugars: 8g

Chapter 6: Energy-Boosting Juices

Morning Kickstarters

Sunrise Ginger Spark

- **Preparation Time:** 10 minutes
- **Ingredients:** 1 orange, peeled; 1 carrot, peeled; 1-inch ginger root; 1/2 lemon, juiced; 1/2 cup water
- **Servings:** 1
- **Preparation Method:** Juicing
- **Procedure:** 1. Chop the orange and carrot into pieces. 2. Juice the orange, carrot, and ginger root. 3. Stir in the lemon juice and water. 4. Serve immediately for a zesty morning boost.
- **Nutritional Values (per serving):** Calories: 95 kcal, Protein: 1.5g, Carbohydrates: 22g, Fat: 0.3g, Fiber: 4g, Sugars: 17g

Avocado & Spinach Power Smoothie

- **Preparation Time:** 5 minutes
- **Ingredients:** 1/2 avocado, 1 cup spinach, 1 banana, 1 cup almond milk, 1 tablespoon chia seeds
- **Servings:** 1
- **Preparation Method:** Blending
- **Procedure:** 1. Combine avocado, spinach, banana, and almond milk in a blender. 2. Blend until smooth. 3. Stir in chia seeds. 4. Enjoy this creamy, energizing smoothie.
- **Nutritional Values (per serving):** Calories: 245 kcal, Protein: 4g, Carbohydrates: 31g, Fat: 12g, Fiber: 9g, Sugars: 15g

Beetroot Citrus Booster

- **Preparation Time:** 10 minutes
- **Ingredients:** 1 small beetroot, 1/2 grapefruit, 1/2 lemon, juiced, 1/4-inch ginger root, 1 cup water
- **Servings:** 2
- **Preparation Method:** Juicing
- **Procedure:** 1. Peel and chop beetroot, grapefruit, and ginger. 2. Juice all ingredients together. 3. Add lemon juice and water. 4. Stir well and serve for a refreshing start.

- **Nutritional Values (per serving):** Calories: 60 kcal, Protein: 1g, Carbohydrates: 14g, Fat: 0.2g, Fiber: 3g, Sugars: 11g

Green Tea Apple Zest

- **Preparation Time:** 15 minutes
- **Ingredients:** 1 green tea bag, 1 apple, 1/2 cucumber, 1 teaspoon honey, 2 cups hot water
- **Servings:** 2
- **Preparation Method:** Infusion and blending
- **Procedure:** 1. Steep green tea in hot water for 5 minutes. 2. Blend apple and cucumber in a blender. 3. Mix the blended fruits with green tea. 4. Add honey for sweetness and serve.
- **Nutritional Values (per serving):** Calories: 50 kcal, Protein: 0.5g, Carbohydrates: 12g, Fat: 0.2g, Fiber: 2g, Sugars: 10g

Midday Energy Elixirs

Tropical Turmeric Reviver

- **Preparation Time:** 10 minutes
- **Ingredients:** 1/2 cup pineapple chunks, 1/2 mango, peeled and diced, 1/2-inch turmeric root, 1/2 cup coconut water, 1 tablespoon lime juice
- **Servings:** 1
- **Preparation Method:** Blending
- **Procedure:** 1. Combine pineapple, mango, and turmeric root in a blender. 2. Pour in coconut water for hydration. 3. Add lime juice for a citrusy kick. 4. Blend until smooth and enjoy this rejuvenating tropical mix.
- **Nutritional Values (per serving):** Calories: 120 kcal, Protein: 1g, Carbohydrates: 30g, Fat: 0.5g, Fiber: 3g, Sugars: 25g

Green Energy Boost

- **Preparation Time:** 8 minutes
- **Ingredients:** 1 cup spinach, 1/2 green apple, cored, 1/2 cucumber, 1/4 cup parsley, 1 cup water
- **Servings:** 1
- **Preparation Method:** Juicing
- **Procedure:** 1. Juice spinach, green apple, and cucumber together. 2. Add parsley for an extra nutrient punch. 3. Mix with water for a lighter consistency. 4. Serve this green elixir for a midday energy surge.
- **Nutritional Values (per serving):** Calories: 60 kcal, Protein: 2g, Carbohydrates: 14g, Fat: 0.3g, Fiber: 3g, Sugars: 9g

Citrus Beet Booster

- **Preparation Time:** 12 minutes
- **Ingredients:** 1 small beetroot, 1/2 orange, peeled, 1/2 lemon, juiced, 1-inch ginger root, 1 cup water
- **Servings:** 2
- **Preparation Method:** Juicing
- **Procedure:** 1. Peel and chop beetroot and ginger. 2. Juice beetroot, orange, and ginger together. 3. Stir in fresh lemon juice and water. 4. Enjoy this zesty and refreshing juice for an instant lift.
- **Nutritional Values (per serving):** Calories: 70 kcal, Protein: 1g, Carbohydrates: 17g, Fat: 0.2g, Fiber: 4g, Sugars: 12g

Berry Almond Bliss

- **Preparation Time:** 5 minutes
- **Ingredients:** 1/2 cup blueberries, 1/2 cup raspberries, 1/2 banana, 1 cup almond milk, 1 teaspoon flax seeds
- **Servings:** 1
- **Preparation Method:** Blending
- **Procedure:** 1. Add blueberries, raspberries, and banana to a blender. 2. Pour in almond milk for a creamy texture. 3. Sprinkle in flax seeds for added fiber. 4. Blend until smooth and savor this berrylicious energy booster.
- **Nutritional Values (per serving):** Calories: 150 kcal, Protein: 3g, Carbohydrates: 28g, Fat: 4.5g, Fiber: 6g, Sugars: 16g

Pre-Workout Power Juices

Apple Beet Performance Enhancer

- **Preparation Time:** 10 minutes
- **Ingredients:** 1 beetroot, 1 apple, 1 carrot, 1/2-inch ginger, 1 cup water
- **Servings:** 1
- **Preparation Method:** Juicing
- **Procedure:** 1. Peel and chop beetroot, apple, carrot, and ginger. 2. Juice all the ingredients together. 3. Dilute with water for a smoother consistency. 4. Consume before workout for an energy boost.
- **Nutritional Values (per serving):** Calories: 110 kcal, Protein: 2g, Carbohydrates: 26g, Fat: 0.3g, Fiber: 5g, Sugars: 18g

Citrus Kick Juice

- **Preparation Time:** 8 minutes
- **Ingredients:** 1 orange, peeled; 1/2 grapefruit, peeled; 1/4 lemon, peeled; 1 teaspoon chia seeds, 1 cup cold water
- **Servings:** 2
- **Preparation Method:** Juicing
- **Procedure:** 1. Juice orange, grapefruit, and lemon. 2. Mix in chia seeds and cold water. 3. Stir well and drink immediately for a refreshing and energizing boost.
- **Nutritional Values (per serving):** Calories: 60 kcal, Protein: 1g, Carbohydrates: 14g, Fat: 0.5g, Fiber: 3g, Sugars: 11g

Pineapple Spinach Power Smoothie

- **Preparation Time:** 5 minutes
- **Ingredients:** 1 cup spinach, 1/2 cup pineapple chunks, 1 banana, 1 tablespoon flaxseed, 1 cup almond milk
- **Servings:** 1
- **Preparation Method:** Blending
- **Procedure:** 1. Add spinach, pineapple, banana, and flaxseed into the blender. 2. Pour in almond milk. 3. Blend until smooth. 4. Enjoy this nutrient-rich smoothie for sustained energy.
- **Nutritional Values (per serving):** Calories: 155 kcal, Protein: 3g, Carbohydrates: 30g, Fat: 4g, Fiber: 5g, Sugars: 20g

Matcha Energy Booster

- **Preparation Time:** 5 minutes
- **Ingredients:** 1 teaspoon matcha powder, 1/2 banana, 1/2 cup Greek yogurt, 1 cup coconut water, 1 tablespoon honey
- **Servings:** 1
- **Preparation Method:** Blending

- **Procedure:** 1. Blend matcha powder, banana, and Greek yogurt. 2. Add coconut water for hydration. 3. Sweeten with honey. 4. Blend until creamy. 5. Serve as a pre-workout energizer.
- **Nutritional Values (per serving):** Calories: 180 kcal, Protein: 10g, Carbohydrates: 35g, Fat: 1g, Fiber: 3g, Sugars: 28g

Chapter 7: Immunity-Boosting Juices

Vitamin-Packed Recipes

Kiwi Kale Vitamin Booster

- **Preparation Time:** 8 minutes
- **Ingredients:** 2 kiwis, peeled; 1 cup kale leaves, 1/2 apple, 1/4 lemon, juiced; 1/2 cup water
- **Servings:** 1
- **Preparation Method:** Juicing

- **Procedure:** 1. Chop kiwis and apple into pieces. 2. Juice kiwis, kale, and apple together. 3. Stir in the lemon juice and water. 4. Enjoy this nutrient-packed drink for a vitamin boost.
- **Nutritional Values (per serving):** Calories: 90 kcal, Protein: 2g, Carbohydrates: 21g, Fat: 0.5g, Fiber: 4g, Sugars: 15g

Carrot-Orange Immunity Mix

- **Preparation Time:** 10 minutes
- **Ingredients:** 2 carrots, 1 orange, peeled; 1-inch ginger root; 1/2 cup water
- **Servings:** 1
- **Preparation Method:** Juicing
- **Procedure:** 1. Peel and chop carrots and ginger. 2. Juice carrots, orange, and ginger. 3. Add water for desired consistency. 4. Drink up for a vibrant vitamin C and A infusion.
- **Nutritional Values (per serving):** Calories: 100 kcal, Protein: 2g, Carbohydrates: 23g, Fat: 0.3g, Fiber: 6g, Sugars: 17g

Recipe 3: Berry Blast Antioxidant Shake

- **Preparation Time:** 5 minutes
- **Ingredients:** 1/2 cup blueberries, 1/2 cup strawberries, 1/2 banana, 1 cup spinach, 1 cup almond milk
- **Servings:** 1
- **Preparation Method:** Blending
- **Procedure:** 1. Blend blueberries, strawberries, banana, and spinach. 2. Add almond milk for a smooth texture. 3. Blend until creamy. 4. Serve this antioxidant-rich shake for a healthful treat.
- **Nutritional Values (per serving):** Calories: 150 kcal, Protein: 3g, Carbohydrates: 31g, Fat: 3g, Fiber: 5g, Sugars: 20g

Green Tea Citrus Fusion

- **Preparation Time:** 15 minutes
- **Ingredients:** 1 green tea bag, 1/2 grapefruit, peeled; 1/4 lemon, peeled; 1 teaspoon honey; 2 cups hot water
- **Servings:** 2
- **Preparation Method:** Infusion
- **Procedure:** 1. Steep green tea bag in hot water for 5 minutes. 2. Squeeze juice from grapefruit and lemon into tea. 3. Stir in honey for sweetness. 4. Enjoy this refreshing and vitamin-packed infusion.
- **Nutritional Values (per serving):** Calories: 35 kcal, Protein: 0.5g, Carbohydrates: 9g, Fat: 0g, Fiber: 1g, Sugars: 8g

Antioxidant-Rich Blends

Pomegranate Blueberry Bliss

- **Preparation Time:** 10 minutes
- **Ingredients:** 1/2 cup pomegranate seeds, 1/2 cup blueberries, 1 apple, 1/2 cup spinach, 1 cup water
- **Servings:** 1
- **Preparation Method:** Blending
- **Procedure:** 1. Blend pomegranate seeds, blueberries, and apple. 2. Add spinach and water for a smooth consistency. 3. Blend until completely smooth. 4. Enjoy this rich antioxidant blend.
- **Nutritional Values (per serving):** Calories: 130 kcal, Protein: 2g, Carbohydrates: 31g, Fat: 0.5g, Fiber: 5g, Sugars: 22g

Acai Antioxidant Power

- **Preparation Time:** 5 minutes
- **Ingredients:** 1 tablespoon acai powder, 1 banana, 1/2 cup mixed berries, 1 cup coconut water
- **Servings:** 1
- **Preparation Method:** Blending
- **Procedure:** 1. Combine acai powder, banana, and mixed berries in a blender. 2. Add coconut water for hydration. 3. Blend until creamy. 4. Savor this superfood-packed drink.
- **Nutritional Values (per serving):** Calories: 180 kcal, Protein: 2g, Carbohydrates: 42g, Fat: 1g, Fiber: 6g, Sugars: 30g

Green Matcha Mixer

- **Preparation Time:** 7 minutes
- **Ingredients:** 1 teaspoon matcha powder, 1/2 banana, 1/2 cup kale, 1/2 cup spinach, 1 cup almond milk
- **Servings:** 1
- **Preparation Method:** Blending
- **Procedure:** 1. Blend matcha powder with banana, kale, and spinach. 2. Add almond milk to achieve a smooth texture. 3. Blend until smooth. 4. Drink this green tea-infused smoothie for a nutrient boost.
- **Nutritional Values (per serving):** Calories: 150 kcal, Protein: 4g, Carbohydrates: 29g, Fat: 3g, Fiber: 4g, Sugars: 17g

Cherry Almond Antioxidant Shake

- **Preparation Time:** 6 minutes
- **Ingredients:** 1/2 cup cherries, pitted, 1/4 cup raw almonds, 1 cup almond milk, 1/2 teaspoon vanilla extract
- **Servings:** 1
- **Preparation Method:** Blending
- **Procedure:** 1. Blend cherries and raw almonds together. 2. Pour in almond milk and add vanilla extract. 3. Blend until smooth and creamy. 4. Enjoy this delicious and healthy shake.
- **Nutritional Values (per serving):** Calories: 200 kcal, Protein: 5g, Carbohydrates: 18g, Fat: 12g, Fiber: 3g, Sugars: 12g

---

Cold and Flu Fighters

Ginger Lemonade Soother

- **Preparation Time:** 10 minutes
- **Ingredients:** 1-inch ginger root, 1 lemon, juiced, 1 tablespoon honey, 2 cups hot water
- **Servings:** 2
- **Preparation Method:** Infusion
- **Procedure:** 1. Grate ginger and add to a jug. 2. Pour in hot water and let it steep for 5 minutes. 3. Stir in fresh lemon juice and honey. 4. Strain and serve warm to soothe cold symptoms.
- **Nutritional Values (per serving):** Calories: 40 kcal, Protein: 0.1g, Carbohydrates: 10g, Fat: 0g, Fiber: 0.2g, Sugars: 9g

Turmeric Pineapple Immunity Boost

- **Preparation Time:** 8 minutes
- **Ingredients:** 1 cup pineapple chunks, 1/2 teaspoon turmeric powder, 1/2 cup orange juice, 1 cup water
- **Servings:** 1
- **Preparation Method:** Blending
- **Procedure:** 1. Blend pineapple chunks with turmeric powder. 2. Add orange juice and water for a smoother blend. 3. Serve chilled to support immune function and combat flu symptoms.
- **Nutritional Values (per serving):** Calories: 120 kcal, Protein: 1g, Carbohydrates: 29g, Fat: 0.5g, Fiber: 3g, Sugars: 22g

Berry Echinacea Elixir

- **Preparation Time:** 5 minutes
- **Ingredients:** 1/2 cup strawberries, 1/2 cup blueberries, 1/4 cup echinacea tea (cooled), 1 teaspoon honey
- **Servings:** 1
- **Preparation Method:** Blending
- **Procedure:** 1. Blend strawberries and blueberries with echinacea tea. 2. Sweeten with honey. 3. Drink this berry blend for its immune-boosting properties during cold and flu season.
- **Nutritional Values (per serving):** Calories: 90 kcal, Protein: 1g, Carbohydrates: 21g, Fat: 0.3g, Fiber: 3g, Sugars: 17g

Spicy Citrus Defense

- **Preparation Time:** 7 minutes
- **Ingredients:** 1/2 grapefruit, peeled, 1/4 lime, juiced, 1/4 teaspoon cayenne pepper, 1 teaspoon honey, 1 cup water
- **Servings:** 1
- **Preparation Method:** Juicing
- **Procedure:** 1. Juice grapefruit and lime. 2. Add cayenne pepper and honey to the juice. 3. Dilute with water as needed. 4. Consume this spicy drink to help fend off cold symptoms.

- **Nutritional Values (per serving):** Calories: 70 kcal, Protein: 1g, Carbohydrates: 18g, Fat: 0.2g, Fiber: 2g, Sugars: 16g

Chapter 8: Digestive Health Juices

Soothing Digestive Aids

Minty Fennel Digestive Soother

- **Preparation Time:** 10 minutes
- **Ingredients:** 1 fennel bulb, 1/4 cup mint leaves, 1/2 lemon, juiced, 1 cup water
- **Servings:** 1
- **Preparation Method:** Juicing

- **Procedure:** 1. Chop fennel bulb and add to the juicer. 2. Juice mint leaves with fennel. 3. Stir in fresh lemon juice and water. 4. Drink to aid digestion and soothe the stomach.
- **Nutritional Values (per serving):** Calories: 50 kcal, Protein: 2g, Carbohydrates: 12g, Fat: 0.1g, Fiber: 3g, Sugars: 7g

Papaya Ginger Calmer

- **Preparation Time:** 7 minutes
- **Ingredients:** 1 cup papaya, 1-inch ginger root, 1/2 cup coconut water, 1 teaspoon lime juice
- **Servings:** 1
- **Preparation Method:** Blending
- **Procedure:** 1. Blend papaya and ginger root. 2. Add coconut water and lime juice for a tropical twist. 3. Serve this soothing drink for digestive health.
- **Nutritional Values (per serving):** Calories: 80 kcal, Protein: 1g, Carbohydrates: 19g, Fat: 0.2g, Fiber: 2g, Sugars: 14g

Cucumber Aloe Cooler

- **Preparation Time:** 5 minutes
- **Ingredients:** 1/2 cucumber, 2 tablespoons aloe vera gel, 1 cup water, 1 teaspoon honey
- **Servings:** 1
- **Preparation Method:** Blending
- **Procedure:** 1. Blend cucumber and aloe vera gel together. 2. Add water and honey to sweeten. 3. Drink this cooling mixture to alleviate digestive discomfort.

- **Nutritional Values (per serving):** Calories: 45 kcal, Protein: 0.5g, Carbohydrates: 11g, Fat: 0.1g, Fiber: 1g, Sugars: 9g

Apple Celery Digestive Aid

- **Preparation Time:** 8 minutes
- **Ingredients:** 1 apple, 2 celery stalks, 1/4-inch ginger root, 1 cup water
- **Servings:** 1
- **Preparation Method:** Juicing
- **Procedure:** 1. Juice apple, celery, and ginger root. 2. Dilute with water as needed. 3. Consume this gentle blend for its digestive benefits.
- **Nutritional Values (per serving):** Calories: 60 kcal, Protein: 1g, Carbohydrates: 14g, Fat: 0.2g, Fiber: 3g, Sugars: 10g

Fiber-Rich Juices

Apple-Pear Fiber Booster

- **Preparation Time:** 10 minutes
- **Ingredients:** 1 apple, 1 pear, 1/4 cup rolled oats, 1 tablespoon flaxseeds, 1 cup water
- **Servings:** 1
- **Preparation Method:** Blending
- **Procedure:** 1. Core and chop the apple and pear. 2. Blend with rolled oats and flaxseeds. 3. Add water for desired consistency. 4. Enjoy this high-fiber drink for digestive health.
- **Nutritional Values (per serving):** Calories: 210 kcal, Protein: 3g, Carbohydrates: 45g, Fat: 4g, Fiber: 9g, Sugars: 25g

Berry Chia Digestive Mix

- **Preparation Time:** 5 minutes
- **Ingredients:** 1/2 cup blueberries, 1/2 cup raspberries, 2 tablespoons chia seeds, 1 cup almond milk
- **Servings:** 1
- **Preparation Method:** Blending
- **Procedure:** 1. Combine berries and chia seeds in a blender. 2. Pour in almond milk. 3. Blend until smooth. 4. This berry-chia combo aids in digestion.
- **Nutritional Values (per serving):** Calories: 180 kcal, Protein: 4g, Carbohydrates: 24g, Fat: 8g, Fiber: 10g, Sugars: 12g

Carrot-Ginger Fiber Fix

- **Preparation Time:** 8 minutes
- **Ingredients:** 2 carrots, 1-inch ginger root, 1/2 lemon, juiced, 1 tablespoon pumpkin seeds, 1 cup water
- **Servings:** 1
- **Preparation Method:** Juicing
- **Procedure:** 1. Juice carrots and ginger root. 2. Add lemon juice. 3. Stir in pumpkin seeds. 4. Dilute with water. 5. This mix supports a healthy digestive system.
- **Nutritional Values (per serving):** Calories: 110 kcal, Protein: 3g, Carbohydrates: 22g, Fat: 2g, Fiber: 6g, Sugars: 10g

Spinach Avocado Fiber Blend

- **Preparation Time:** 7 minutes
- **Ingredients:** 1 cup spinach, 1/2 avocado, 1/2 banana, 1 tablespoon hemp seeds, 1 cup coconut water
- **Servings:** 1
- **Preparation Method:** Blending
- **Procedure:** 1. Blend spinach, avocado, and banana. 2. Add hemp seeds for added fiber. 3. Use coconut water to thin the mixture. 4. Drink this blend for digestive wellness.
- **Nutritional Values (per serving):** Calories: 220 kcal, Protein: 5g, Carbohydrates: 27g, Fat: 12g, Fiber: 7g, Sugars: 14g

Gut-Healthy Probiotic Mixes

Kefir Kale Smoothie

- **Preparation Time:** 5 minutes
- **Ingredients:** 1 cup plain kefir, 1/2 cup kale, 1 banana, 1 tablespoon honey
- **Servings:** 1
- **Preparation Method:** Blending
- **Procedure:** 1. Combine kefir, kale, and banana in a blender. 2. Add honey for sweetness. 3. Blend until smooth. 4. Enjoy this probiotic-rich, gut-friendly smoothie.
- **Nutritional Values (per serving):** Calories: 200 kcal, Protein: 9g, Carbohydrates: 40g, Fat: 2.5g, Fiber: 3g, Sugars: 25g

Probiotic Berry Blast

- **Preparation Time:** 6 minutes
- **Ingredients:** 1 cup Greek yogurt, 1/2 cup mixed berries, 1 tablespoon chia seeds, 1 teaspoon maple syrup
- **Servings:** 1
- **Preparation Method:** Blending
- **Procedure:** 1. Blend Greek yogurt with mixed berries. 2. Stir in chia seeds and maple syrup. 3. This berry-yogurt mix promotes healthy digestion with probiotics.
- **Nutritional Values (per serving):** Calories: 180 kcal, Protein: 11g, Carbohydrates: 24g, Fat: 4g, Fiber: 5g, Sugars: 15g

Apple-Cinnamon Probiotic Drink

- **Preparation Time:** 7 minutes
- **Ingredients:** 1 cup apple cider, 1/2 teaspoon ground cinnamon, 1/2 cup kefir, 1 teaspoon honey

- **Servings:** 1
- **Preparation Method:** Mixing
- **Procedure:** 1. Mix apple cider with cinnamon. 2. Add kefir and honey. 3. Stir well. 4. This apple-cinnamon concoction is great for gut health.
- **Nutritional Values (per serving):** Calories: 140 kcal, Protein: 4g, Carbohydrates: 29g, Fat: 1g, Fiber: 1g, Sugars: 27g

Mango Lassi Probiotic Smoothie

- **Preparation Time:** 8 minutes
- **Ingredients:** 1 cup ripe mango, cubed, 1/2 cup plain yogurt, 1/4 teaspoon cardamom powder, 1 cup water
- **Servings:** 1
- **Preparation Method:** Blending
- **Procedure:** 1. Blend mango and yogurt. 2. Add cardamom powder for flavor. 3. Thin with water as needed. 4. Savor this traditional Indian lassi for digestive health.
- **Nutritional Values (per serving):** Calories: 190 kcal, Protein: 5g, Carbohydrates: 38g, Fat: 2g, Fiber: 3g, Sugars: 34g

Chapter 9: Heart-Healthy Juices

Cholesterol-Lowering Recipes

Oatmeal Almond Smoothie

- **Preparation Time:** 8 minutes
- **Ingredients:** 1/2 cup rolled oats, 1 cup almond milk, 1 banana, 1 tablespoon honey, 1/4 teaspoon cinnamon
- **Servings:** 1
- **Preparation Method:** Blending
- **Procedure:** 1. Soak oats in almond milk for 5 minutes. 2. Add banana, honey, and cinnamon to the mix. 3. Blend until smooth. 4. This heart-healthy smoothie helps lower cholesterol.
- **Nutritional Values (per serving):** Calories: 220 kcal, Protein: 5g, Carbohydrates: 40g, Fat: 4g, Fiber: 5g, Sugars: 20g

Red Berry Flaxseed Juice

- **Preparation Time:** 5 minutes
- **Ingredients:** 1 cup mixed red berries (strawberries, raspberries), 2 tablespoons ground flaxseed, 1 cup water, 1 teaspoon lemon juice
- **Servings:** 1
- **Preparation Method:** Blending
- **Procedure:** 1. Blend berries with water and lemon juice. 2. Stir in ground flaxseed. 3. Serve chilled for a delicious cholesterol-lowering drink.
- **Nutritional Values (per serving):** Calories: 130 kcal, Protein: 3g, Carbohydrates: 20g, Fat: 5g, Fiber: 8g, Sugars: 10g

Green Tea Citrus Infusion

- **Preparation Time:** 10 minutes
- **Ingredients:** 1 green tea bag, 1/2 orange, sliced, 1/4 lemon, sliced, 1 tablespoon honey, 1 cup hot water
- **Servings:** 1
- **Preparation Method:** Infusing
- **Procedure:** 1. Steep green tea bag in hot water for 5 minutes. 2. Add orange and lemon slices. 3. Sweeten with honey. 4. This infusion is ideal for reducing cholesterol.

- **Nutritional Values (per serving):** Calories: 60 kcal, Protein: 0.5g, Carbohydrates: 15g, Fat: 0g, Fiber: 2g, Sugars: 12g

Avocado Spinach Smoothie

- **Preparation Time:** 7 minutes
- **Ingredients:** 1/2 avocado, 1 cup spinach, 1/2 cup Greek yogurt, 1 cup water, 1 teaspoon chia seeds
- **Servings:** 1
- **Preparation Method:** Blending
- **Procedure:** 1. Blend avocado, spinach, and Greek yogurt. 2. Add water to achieve desired consistency. 3. Stir in chia seeds. 4. This smoothie is a powerhouse for lowering cholesterol.
- **Nutritional Values (per serving):** Calories: 240 kcal, Protein: 8g, Carbohydrates: 20g, Fat: 15g, Fiber: 7g, Sugars: 5g

Blood Pressure Balancers

Celery Cucumber Cooler

- **Preparation Time:** 10 minutes
- **Ingredients:** 2 stalks celery, 1 cucumber, 1/2 green apple, 1 tablespoon lemon juice, 1 cup water
- **Servings:** 1
- **Preparation Method:** Juicing
- **Procedure:** 1. Juice celery, cucumber, and green apple together. 2. Stir in lemon juice. 3. Dilute with water as needed. 4. This refreshing drink helps in managing blood pressure.
- **Nutritional Values (per serving):** Calories: 80 kcal, Protein: 2g, Carbohydrates: 18g, Fat: 0g, Fiber: 4g, Sugars: 12g

Beetroot Ginger Blast

- **Preparation Time:** 12 minutes
- **Ingredients:** 1 medium beetroot, 1 inch ginger, 1 carrot, 1/2 lemon, peeled, 1 cup water
- **Servings:** 1
- **Preparation Method:** Juicing
- **Procedure:** 1. Juice beetroot, ginger, and carrot. 2. Squeeze in lemon juice. 3. Add water to adjust consistency. 4.

This potent juice aids in blood pressure regulation.

- **Nutritional Values (per serving):** Calories: 90 kcal, Protein: 3g, Carbohydrates: 21g, Fat: 0.5g, Fiber: 5g, Sugars: 15g

Pomegranate Parsley Power

- **Preparation Time:** 8 minutes
- **Ingredients:** 1/2 cup pomegranate seeds, 1/4 cup parsley, 1/2 apple, 1 cup water
- **Servings:** 1
- **Preparation Method:** Blending
- **Procedure:** 1. Blend pomegranate seeds, parsley, and apple. 2. Add water for desired consistency. 3. This blend is effective for maintaining healthy blood pressure.
- **Nutritional Values (per serving):** Calories: 100 kcal, Protein: 2g, Carbohydrates: 23g, Fat: 1g, Fiber: 6g, Sugars: 16g

Spinach Kiwi Kalm

- **Preparation Time:** 7 minutes
- **Ingredients:** 1 cup spinach, 2 kiwis, peeled, 1/2 lime, juiced, 1 teaspoon honey, 1 cup water

- **Servings:** 1
- **Preparation Method:** Blending
- **Procedure:** 1. Blend spinach and kiwis. 2. Add lime juice and honey. 3. Mix in water as needed. 4. Enjoy this vitamin-rich juice for blood pressure control.
- **Nutritional Values (per serving):** Calories: 120 kcal, Protein: 3g, Carbohydrates: 28g, Fat: 1g, Fiber: 5g, Sugars: 20g

---

Heart-Protective Blends

Walnut Blueberry Bliss

- **Preparation Time:** 10 minutes
- **Ingredients:** 1/2 cup blueberries, 1/4 cup walnuts, 1 cup spinach, 1 tablespoon flaxseeds, 1 cup almond milk
- **Servings:** 1
- **Preparation Method:** Blending
- **Procedure:** 1. Combine blueberries, walnuts, spinach, and flaxseeds in a blender. 2. Pour in almond milk. 3. Blend until smooth. 4. This heart-healthy juice is rich in antioxidants and Omega-3s.
- **Nutritional Values (per serving):** Calories: 220 kcal, Protein: 6g, Carbohydrates: 18g, Fat: 15g, Fiber: 5g, Sugars: 8g

Omega Orange Medley

- **Preparation Time:** 8 minutes
- **Ingredients:** 2 oranges, peeled, 1/4 cup chia seeds, 1/2 carrot, 1 teaspoon turmeric, 1 cup water
- **Servings:** 1
- **Preparation Method:** Juicing
- **Procedure:** 1. Juice oranges and carrot. 2. Stir in chia seeds and turmeric. 3. Add water to achieve desired consistency. 4. This blend supports heart health with its high Omega-3 and vitamin content.
- **Nutritional Values (per serving):** Calories: 180 kcal, Protein: 4g, Carbohydrates: 33g, Fat: 5g, Fiber: 7g, Sugars: 20g

Avocado Apple Affair

- **Preparation Time:** 12 minutes
- **Ingredients:** 1/2 avocado, 1 green apple, 1/2 cucumber, 1 tablespoon lemon juice, 1 cup coconut water
- **Servings:** 1
- **Preparation Method:** Blending
- **Procedure:** 1. Blend avocado, green apple, and cucumber. 2. Mix in lemon juice. 3. Add coconut water for consistency. 4. This creamy juice is excellent for heart health, providing healthy fats and hydration.
- **Nutritional Values (per serving):** Calories: 200 kcal, Protein: 3g, Carbohydrates: 27g, Fat: 10g, Fiber: 7g, Sugars: 15g

Kale Kiwi Kardia

- **Preparation Time:** 10 minutes
- **Ingredients:** 1 cup kale, 2 kiwis, peeled, 1/4 cup mixed berries, 1 tablespoon hemp seeds, 1 cup green tea
- **Servings:** 1
- **Preparation Method:** Blending
- **Procedure:** 1. Combine kale, kiwis, and berries in a blender. 2. Add hemp seeds. 3. Pour in brewed green tea. 4. Blend to a smooth consistency. 5. This drink is packed with heart-friendly antioxidants and nutrients.
- **Nutritional Values (per serving):** Calories: 150 kcal, Protein: 5g, Carbohydrates: 25g, Fat: 4g, Fiber: 6g, Sugars: 14g

Chapter 10: Skin and Beauty Juices

Radiant Skin Recipes

Cucumber Mint Refresher

- **Preparation Time:** 10 minutes
- **Ingredients:** 1 large cucumber, 1/2 cup mint leaves, 1/2 apple, 1 tablespoon lime juice, 1 cup water
- **Servings:** 2
- **Preparation Method:** Juicing

- **Procedure:** 1. Juice cucumber, mint leaves, and apple. 2. Stir in lime juice. 3. Add water to thin the juice if desired. 4. This refreshing drink hydrates and nourishes the skin.
- **Nutritional Values (per serving):** Calories: 50 kcal, Protein: 1g, Carbohydrates: 12g, Fat: 0g, Fiber: 2g, Sugars: 8g

Carrot Ginger Glow

- **Preparation Time:** 8 minutes
- **Ingredients:** 3 carrots, 1-inch ginger root, 1/2 orange, peeled, 1 teaspoon honey (optional), 1 cup water
- **Servings:** 1
- **Preparation Method:** Juicing
- **Procedure:** 1. Juice carrots, ginger, and orange. 2. Mix in honey for sweetness if needed. 3. Dilute with water as required. 4. This vibrant juice is rich in vitamin A and antioxidants for healthy skin.
- **Nutritional Values (per serving):** Calories: 110 kcal, Protein: 2g, Carbohydrates: 26g, Fat: 0.5g, Fiber: 6g, Sugars: 18g

Berry Basil Bliss

- **Preparation Time:** 12 minutes
- **Ingredients:** 1 cup mixed berries (strawberries, blueberries, raspberries), 1/4 cup basil leaves, 1 cup coconut water, 1 tablespoon chia seeds
- **Servings:** 1
- **Preparation Method:** Blending
- **Procedure:** 1. Blend berries and basil leaves together. 2. Add coconut water for hydration. 3. Stir in chia seeds for texture. 4. This antioxidant-rich juice promotes glowing, youthful skin.
- **Nutritional Values (per serving):** Calories: 130 kcal, Protein: 3g, Carbohydrates: 25g, Fat: 3g, Fiber: 5g, Sugars: 15g

Avocado Citrus Cream

- **Preparation Time:** 10 minutes
- **Ingredients:** 1/2 ripe avocado, 1/2 grapefruit, peeled, 1/2 lemon, juiced, 1 cup spinach, 1 cup almond milk
- **Servings:** 1
- **Preparation Method:** Blending
- **Procedure:** 1. Blend avocado, grapefruit, lemon juice, and spinach. 2. Add almond milk for a creamy consistency. 3. This smoothie is packed with healthy fats and vitamin C for skin health.
- **Nutritional Values (per serving):** Calories: 200 kcal, Protein: 4g, Carbohydrates: 20g, Fat: 12g, Fiber: 7g, Sugars: 8g

Anti-Aging Juices

Pomegranate Blueberry Potion

- **Preparation Time:** 10 minutes
- **Ingredients:** 1 cup pomegranate seeds, 1 cup blueberries, 1/2 banana, 1 tablespoon flaxseeds, 1 cup water
- **Servings:** 2
- **Preparation Method:** Blending
- **Procedure:** 1. Blend pomegranate seeds, blueberries, and banana. 2. Stir in flaxseeds. 3. Add water to reach desired consistency. 4. Enjoy this antioxidant-packed juice for youthful skin.
- **Nutritional Values (per serving):** Calories: 120 kcal, Protein: 2g, Carbohydrates: 28g, Fat: 2g, Fiber: 4g, Sugars: 18g

Golden Turmeric Elixir

- **Preparation Time:** 8 minutes
- **Ingredients:** 1/2 cup pineapple chunks, 1 carrot, 1 inch turmeric root, 1/2 lemon, juiced, 1 cup coconut water
- **Servings:** 1
- **Preparation Method:** Juicing
- **Procedure:** 1. Juice pineapple, carrot, and turmeric root. 2. Add lemon juice. 3. Mix with coconut water. 4. This vibrant juice is rich in anti-inflammatory properties, ideal for anti-aging.
- **Nutritional Values (per serving):** Calories: 100 kcal, Protein: 1g, Carbohydrates: 23g, Fat: 0.5g, Fiber: 3g, Sugars: 17g

Avocado Green Smoothie

- **Preparation Time:** 12 minutes
- **Ingredients:** 1/2 avocado, 1 cup spinach, 1/2 apple, 1 tablespoon almond butter, 1 cup almond milk
- **Servings:** 1
- **Preparation Method:** Blending
- **Procedure:** 1. Blend avocado, spinach, apple, and almond butter. 2. Add almond milk for creaminess. 3. This smoothie is loaded with healthy fats and vitamins for skin elasticity.
- **Nutritional Values (per serving):** Calories: 200 kcal, Protein: 3g, Carbohydrates: 20g, Fat: 12g, Fiber: 6g, Sugars: 10g

Red Radiance Booster

- **Preparation Time:** 10 minutes

- **Ingredients:** 1 beetroot, 1/2 cup strawberries, 1/2 orange, peeled, 1 teaspoon chia seeds, 1 cup water
- **Servings:** 2
- **Preparation Method:** Juicing

- **Procedure:** 1. Juice beetroot, strawberries, and orange. 2. Stir in chia seeds. 3. Add water as needed. 4. This juice is excellent for blood circulation, promoting skin health.
- **Nutritional Values (per serving):** Calories: 90 kcal, Protein: 2g, Carbohydrates: 20g, Fat: 1g, Fiber: 3g, Sugars: 14g

Hair and Nail Strengthening Mixes

Silky Strawberry Almond Bliss

- **Preparation Time:** 10 minutes
- **Ingredients:** 1 cup strawberries, 1/2 banana, 2 tablespoons almond butter, 1 tablespoon chia seeds, 1 cup soy milk
- **Servings:** 2
- **Preparation Method:** Blending
- **Procedure:** 1. Combine strawberries, banana, and almond butter in a blender. 2. Add chia seeds for texture. 3. Blend with soy milk until smooth. 4. This mix promotes hair and nail strength with biotin and vitamin E.
- **Nutritional Values (per serving):** Calories: 180 kcal, Protein: 6g, Carbohydrates: 20g, Fat: 10g, Fiber: 5g, Sugars: 10g

Cucumber Spinach Rejuvenator

- **Preparation Time:** 8 minutes
- **Ingredients:** 1 cucumber, 2 cups spinach, 1 apple, 1 tablespoon flaxseed oil, 1 cup water
- **Servings:** 2
- **Preparation Method:** Juicing
- **Procedure:** 1. Juice cucumber, spinach, and apple together. 2. Stir in flaxseed oil for omega-3 fatty acids. 3. Dilute with water as desired. 4. This juice is rich in silica, vital for hair and nail health.
- **Nutritional Values (per serving):** Calories: 110 kcal, Protein: 3g, Carbohydrates: 20g, Fat: 4g, Fiber: 4g, Sugars: 12g

Carrot Avocado Power Drink

- **Preparation Time:** 12 minutes
- **Ingredients:** 2 carrots, 1/2 avocado, 1 teaspoon lemon juice, 1 tablespoon hemp seeds, 1 cup coconut water
- **Servings:** 1
- **Preparation Method:** Blending
- **Procedure:** 1. Blend carrots and avocado for beta-carotene. 2. Add lemon juice and hemp seeds. 3. Combine with coconut water for hydration. 4. Enjoy this nourishing drink, great for strengthening hair and nails.
- **Nutritional Values (per serving):** Calories: 220 kcal, Protein: 5g, Carbohydrates: 30g, Fat: 10g, Fiber: 7g, Sugars: 15g

Walnut Berry Fusion

- **Preparation Time:** 10 minutes
- **Ingredients:** 1/2 cup blueberries, 1/4 cup walnuts, 1/2 banana, 1 teaspoon honey, 1 cup almond milk
- **Servings:** 2
- **Preparation Method:** Blending
- **Procedure:** 1. Blend blueberries, walnuts, and banana for a nutrient-rich mix. 2. Sweeten with honey. 3. Add almond milk for a creamy texture. 4. This fusion is full of antioxidants and omega-3s, excellent for hair and nails.
- **Nutritional Values (per serving):** Calories: 180 kcal, Protein: 4g, Carbohydrates: 24g, Fat: 9g, Fiber: 3g, Sugars: 15g

Chapter 11: Mind and Mood Enhancing Juices

Stress-Relieving Sips

Lavender Lemonade Zen

- **Preparation Time:** 10 minutes
- **Ingredients:** 1 cup fresh lemon juice, 2 tablespoons dried lavender, 3 tablespoons honey, 4 cups water, ice cubes
- **Servings:** 4
- **Preparation Method:** Infusing

- **Procedure:** 1. Boil water and infuse lavender for 5 minutes. 2. Strain and cool lavender water. 3. Stir in lemon juice and honey. 4. Serve over ice for a calming effect.
- **Nutritional Values (per serving):** Calories: 60 kcal, Protein: 0.5g, Carbohydrates: 17g, Fat: 0g, Fiber: 0.2g, Sugars: 16g

Chamomile Apple Elixir

- **Preparation Time:** 12 minutes
- **Ingredients:** 2 chamomile tea bags, 1 cup apple juice, 1 teaspoon ginger, honey (to taste), 2 cups hot water
- **Servings:** 2
- **Preparation Method:** Steeping
- **Procedure:** 1. Steep chamomile and ginger in hot water for 10 minutes. 2. Remove tea bags and add apple juice. 3. Sweeten with honey as desired. 4. Enjoy warm to relieve stress.
- **Nutritional Values (per serving):** Calories: 80 kcal, Protein: 0g, Carbohydrates: 20g, Fat: 0g, Fiber: 0g, Sugars: 18g

Minty Green Relaxer

- **Preparation Time:** 7 minutes
- **Ingredients:** 1 cucumber, 1/2 cup fresh mint leaves, 2 cups spinach, 1 tablespoon lime juice, 1 cup water
- **Servings:** 2
- **Preparation Method:** Juicing
- **Procedure:** 1. Juice cucumber, mint, and spinach together. 2. Stir in lime juice. 3. Add water to dilute as desired. 4. This juice is perfect for reducing stress and refreshing the mind.

- **Nutritional Values (per serving):** Calories: 40 kcal, Protein: 2g, Carbohydrates: 9g, Fat: 0.5g, Fiber: 2g, Sugars: 4g

Berry Basil Bliss

- **Preparation Time:** 8 minutes
- **Ingredients:** 1 cup mixed berries (strawberries, blueberries), 1/4 cup fresh basil leaves, 1 teaspoon honey, 2 cups coconut water
- **Servings:** 2
- **Preparation Method:** Blending
- **Procedure:** 1. Blend berries and basil until smooth. 2. Sweeten with honey. 3. Add coconut water for hydration. 4. Serve chilled for a soothing and refreshing stress-reliever.
- **Nutritional Values (per serving):** Calories: 70 kcal, Protein: 1g, Carbohydrates: 16g, Fat: 0.5g, Fiber: 3g, Sugars: 12g

Mood-Boosting Mixtures

Sunshine Citrus Smoothie

- **Preparation Time:** 10 minutes
- **Ingredients:** 1 orange, peeled; 1/2 cup pineapple chunks; 1/2 banana; 1/2 cup Greek yogurt; 1 teaspoon honey; 1/2 cup almond milk
- **Servings:** 2
- **Preparation Method:** Blending
- **Procedure:** 1. Combine orange, pineapple, and banana in blender. 2. Add Greek yogurt and honey. 3. Pour in almond milk for smooth consistency. 4. Blend until creamy for a mood-enhancing drink.
- **Nutritional Values (per serving):** Calories: 150 kcal, Protein: 5g, Carbohydrates: 28g, Fat: 2g, Fiber: 3g, Sugars: 20g

Berry Bliss Booster

- **Preparation Time:** 7 minutes
- **Ingredients:** 1 cup mixed berries (strawberries, blueberries, raspberries); 1 tablespoon chia seeds; 1 teaspoon vanilla extract; 1 cup coconut water
- **Servings:** 2
- **Preparation Method:** Blending
- **Procedure:** 1. Blend berries and chia seeds together. 2. Add vanilla extract for flavor. 3. Mix in coconut water for hydration. 4. Serve chilled to uplift mood and energy.
- **Nutritional Values (per serving):** Calories: 120 kcal, Protein: 3g, Carbohydrates: 23g, Fat: 2g, Fiber: 5g, Sugars: 15g

Green Mood Lifter

- **Preparation Time:** 8 minutes
- **Ingredients:** 1 cup spinach; 1/2 avocado; 1/2 apple; 1 tablespoon lemon juice; 1 cup water; 1 teaspoon honey (optional)
- **Servings:** 2
- **Preparation Method:** Blending
- **Procedure:** 1. Blend spinach, avocado, and apple. 2. Add lemon juice for zest. 3. Include water for desired consistency. 4. Sweeten with honey if preferred. 5. Enjoy this smoothie for a natural mood boost.
- **Nutritional Values (per serving):** Calories: 130 kcal, Protein: 2g, Carbohydrates: 18g, Fat: 7g, Fiber: 5g, Sugars: 10g

Tropical Happiness Juice

- **Preparation Time:** 5 minutes
- **Ingredients:** 1/2 cup mango chunks; 1/2 cup papaya chunks; 1/2 cup pineapple juice; 1 teaspoon lime juice; 1/2 cup water
- **Servings:** 2
- **Preparation Method:** Juicing/Blending
- **Procedure:** 1. Juice mango and papaya together. 2. Mix in pineapple and lime juice. 3. Dilute with water as needed. 4. This tropical mix is perfect for elevating mood and spirits.
- **Nutritional Values (per serving):** Calories: 100 kcal, Protein: 1g, Carbohydrates: 25g, Fat: 0.5g, Fiber: 2g, Sugars: 20g

Brain-Boosting Beverages

Blueberry Brainwave Smoothie

- **Preparation Time:** 5 minutes
- **Ingredients:** 1 cup blueberries, 1 banana, 1/2 cup spinach, 1 tablespoon flaxseeds, 1 cup almond milk
- **Servings:** 2
- **Preparation Method:** Blending
- **Procedure:** 1. Combine blueberries, banana, and spinach in a blender. 2. Add flaxseeds for omega-3 boost. 3. Pour in almond milk for creamy texture. 4. Blend until smooth for cognitive enhancement.
- **Nutritional Values (per serving):** Calories: 180 kcal, Protein: 4g, Carbohydrates: 33g, Fat: 4g, Fiber: 6g, Sugars: 20g

Avocado & Walnut Elixir

- **Preparation Time:** 6 minutes
- **Ingredients:** 1/2 ripe avocado, 1/4 cup walnuts, 1 teaspoon honey, 1 cup Greek yogurt, 1/2 cup water
- **Servings:** 2
- **Preparation Method:** Blending
- **Procedure:** 1. Scoop avocado into blender. 2. Add walnuts for brain health. 3. Include honey for sweetness. 4. Blend with Greek yogurt and water until smooth. 5. Enjoy for mental sharpness.
- **Nutritional Values (per serving):** Calories: 240 kcal, Protein: 9g, Carbohydrates: 18g, Fat: 16g, Fiber: 4g, Sugars: 10g

Matcha Memory Booster

- **Preparation Time:** 4 minutes
- **Ingredients:** 1 teaspoon matcha powder, 1/2 cup spinach, 1 apple, 1 teaspoon lemon juice, 1 cup coconut water
- **Servings:** 2
- **Preparation Method:** Blending
- **Procedure:** 1. Blend matcha powder and spinach for antioxidants. 2. Add chopped apple for natural sweetness. 3. Squeeze in lemon juice. 4. Mix with coconut water for hydration. 5. Serve this energizing drink.
- **Nutritional Values (per serving):** Calories: 110 kcal, Protein: 2g, Carbohydrates: 25g, Fat: 1g, Fiber: 3g, Sugars: 20g

- **Nutritional Values (per serving):** Calories: 90 kcal, Protein: 1g, Carbohydrates: 22g, Fat: 0.5g, Fiber: 3g, Sugars: 18g

Ginger-Citrus Brain Buzz

- **Preparation Time:** 7 minutes
- **Ingredients:** 1/2-inch ginger, 1 orange (peeled), 1/2 grapefruit (peeled), 1 carrot, 1/2 cup water
- **Servings:** 2
- **Preparation Method:** Juicing
- **Procedure:** 1. Juice ginger, orange, and grapefruit. 2. Add carrot for beta-carotene. 3. Dilute with water for desired consistency. 4. This zesty juice aids in concentration and mental alertness.

Chapter 12: Specialized Juices for Unique Needs

Juices for Athletes and Fitness Enthusiasts

Energizing Beetroot Blast

- **Preparation Time:** 10 minutes
- **Ingredients:** 1 medium beetroot, 1 carrot, 1 apple, 1/2-inch ginger, 1/2 lemon
- **Servings:** 2
- **Preparation Method:** Juicing
- **Procedure:** 1. Chop beetroot, carrot, and apple. 2. Juice with ginger for a kick. 3. Squeeze in lemon for freshness. 4. Serve chilled for an energy boost pre-workout.
- **Nutritional Values (per serving):** Calories: 120 kcal, Protein: 2g, Carbohydrates: 28g, Fat: 0.5g, Fiber: 5g, Sugars: 20g

Spinach Power Potion

- **Preparation Time:** 7 minutes
- **Ingredients:** 2 cups spinach, 1 cucumber, 1 green apple, 1 tablespoon chia seeds, 1 cup coconut water
- **Servings:** 2
- **Preparation Method:** Blending
- **Procedure:** 1. Combine spinach, cucumber, and apple in blender. 2. Add chia seeds for protein. 3. Blend with coconut water for hydration. 4. Enjoy post-workout for recovery.
- **Nutritional Values (per serving):** Calories: 150 kcal, Protein: 4g, Carbohydrates: 30g, Fat: 3g, Fiber: 6g, Sugars: 18g

Citrus Endurance Enhancer

- **Preparation Time:** 5 minutes
- **Ingredients:** 2 oranges, 1/2 grapefruit, 1 teaspoon turmeric, 1 teaspoon honey, 1 cup water
- **Servings:** 2
- **Preparation Method:** Juicing
- **Procedure:** 1. Juice oranges and grapefruit. 2. Stir in turmeric for anti-inflammatory benefits. 3. Add honey for natural sweetness. 4. Dilute with water, drink before endurance training.

- **Nutritional Values (per serving):** Calories: 110 kcal, Protein: 2g, Carbohydrates: 26g, Fat: 0.5g, Fiber: 3g, Sugars: 22g

Banana-Strawberry Protein Smoothie

- **Preparation Time:** 6 minutes
- **Ingredients:** 1 banana, 1/2 cup strawberries, 1 tablespoon almond butter, 1 scoop protein powder, 1 cup almond milk
- **Servings:** 2
- **Preparation Method:** Blending
- **Procedure:** 1. Blend banana and strawberries. 2. Add almond butter and protein powder. 3. Mix with almond milk until smooth. 4. Consume post-strength training for muscle repair.
- **Nutritional Values (per serving):** Calories: 220 kcal, Protein: 15g, Carbohydrates: 30g, Fat: 7g, Fiber: 4g, Sugars: 15g

Juices for Seniors and Children

Gentle Apple Carrot Delight

- **Preparation Time:** 8 minutes
- **Ingredients:** 2 apples, 1 carrot, 1/2 inch ginger, 1/4 teaspoon cinnamon
- **Servings:** 2
- **Preparation Method:** Juicing
- **Procedure:** 1. Core apples, chop carrot. 2. Juice with ginger for a mild zest. 3. Stir in cinnamon for extra flavor. 4. Serve fresh for a nutritious, easy-to-digest drink.
- **Nutritional Values (per serving):** Calories: 95 kcal, Protein: 1g, Carbohydrates: 25g, Fat: 0.3g, Fiber: 5g, Sugars: 18g

Berry Banana Bliss

- **Preparation Time:** 5 minutes
- **Ingredients:** 1 banana, 1/2 cup mixed berries, 1 cup spinach, 1 cup almond milk
- **Servings:** 2
- **Preparation Method:** Blending
- **Procedure:** 1. Peel and slice banana. 2. Blend with berries and spinach. 3. Add almond milk for creaminess. 4. Serve as a nutrient-packed, smooth drink for all ages.

- **Nutritional Values (per serving):** Calories: 120 kcal, Protein: 2g, Carbohydrates: 28g, Fat: 1.5g, Fiber: 4g, Sugars: 15g

Tropical Digestive Aid

- **Preparation Time:** 7 minutes
- **Ingredients:** 1/2 cup pineapple, 1/2 mango, 1/2 cup yogurt, 1 teaspoon flaxseed
- **Servings:** 2
- **Preparation Method:** Blending
- **Procedure:** 1. Chop pineapple and mango. 2. Blend with yogurt for probiotics. 3. Add flaxseed for fiber. 4. Serve chilled for a tropical, digestion-friendly treat.
- **Nutritional Values (per serving):** Calories: 110 kcal, Protein: 3g, Carbohydrates: 22g, Fat: 2g, Fiber: 3g, Sugars: 17g

Soothing Peach Oat Smoothie

- **Preparation Time:** 6 minutes
- **Ingredients:** 1 peach, 1/4 cup oats, 1/2 cup milk, 1 teaspoon honey
- **Servings:** 2
- **Preparation Method:** Blending

- **Procedure:** 1. Slice peach. 2. Blend with oats for a smooth texture. 3. Add milk and honey for sweetness. 4. Serve as a gentle, filling drink perfect for sensitive stomachs.

- **Nutritional Values (per serving):** Calories: 120 kcal, Protein: 4g, Carbohydrates: 24g, Fat: 2g, Fiber: 3g, Sugars: 16g

Seasonal and Exotic Juice Recipes

Dragon Fruit Sunrise

- **Preparation Time:** 10 minutes
- **Ingredients:** 1 dragon fruit, 1/2 cup pineapple chunks, 1 orange (juiced), 1 teaspoon chia seeds
- **Servings:** 2
- **Preparation Method:** Blending
- **Procedure:** 1. Scoop dragon fruit flesh. 2. Blend with pineapple and orange juice. 3. Stir in chia seeds. 4. Serve chilled for an exotic, vitamin-rich start.
- **Nutritional Values (per serving):** Calories: 130 kcal, Protein: 2g, Carbohydrates: 31g, Fat: 1g, Fiber: 4g, Sugars: 24g

Pomegranate Persimmon Potion

- **Preparation Time:** 12 minutes
- **Ingredients:** 1 pomegranate, 2 persimmons, 1/2 lemon (juiced), 1/2-inch ginger

- **Servings:** 2
- **Preparation Method:** Juicing
- **Procedure:** 1. Seed pomegranate. 2. Peel and chop persimmons. 3. Juice with lemon and ginger. 4. Serve fresh for a tangy, nutrient-packed beverage.
- **Nutritional Values (per serving):** Calories: 115 kcal, Protein: 1.5g, Carbohydrates: 28g, Fat: 0.5g, Fiber: 6g, Sugars: 20g

Starfruit Citrus Splash

- **Preparation Time:** 8 minutes
- **Ingredients:** 2 starfruits, 1/2 cup coconut water, 1 lime (juiced), mint leaves
- **Servings:** 2
- **Preparation Method:** Blending
- **Procedure:** 1. Slice starfruits. 2. Blend with coconut water and lime juice. 3. Garnish with mint leaves. 4. Serve as a refreshing, hydrating tropical drink.

- **Nutritional Values (per serving):** Calories: 95 kcal, Protein: 1g, Carbohydrates: 22g, Fat: 0.2g, Fiber: 5g, Sugars: 17g

Lychee Lavender Elixir

- **Preparation Time:** 10 minutes
- **Ingredients:** 1 cup lychees (peeled and pitted), 1/4 cup blueberries, 1/2 teaspoon dried lavender, 1 cup water
- **Servings:** 2
- **Preparation Method:** Blending
- **Procedure:** 1. Blend lychees and blueberries. 2. Infuse with lavender. 3. Add water for consistency. 4. Strain and serve for a fragrant, antioxidant-rich refreshment.
- **Nutritional Values (per serving):** Calories: 80 kcal, Protein: 1g, Carbohydrates: 20g, Fat: 0.1g, Fiber: 2g, Sugars: 15g

Chapter 13: Conclusion and Moving Forward

Reflecting on Your Juicing Journey

As we reach the conclusion of this comprehensive guide to juicing, it's time to reflect on the transformative journey you've embarked upon. Juicing isn't just a culinary activity; it's a lifestyle choice that impacts your health, well-being, and outlook on life. Let's revisit the key milestones and insights that have shaped your juicing journey, helping you to weave this healthful practice seamlessly into your daily routine and continue on your path to wellness.

I. Embracing Change and Celebrating Progress

Your journey began with an introduction to the world of juicing, a step towards embracing a healthier lifestyle. You've learned about the multifaceted benefits of juicing, from detoxifying your body to enhancing your skin's radiance. Remember the excitement of trying your first homemade juice blend? Those initial steps were crucial in setting the foundation for a sustained, health-focused change in your life.

Reflect on the progress you've made since then. Each juice you've prepared has been a testament to your commitment to nourishing yourself and your family. You've not only enhanced your nutritional intake but also discovered creative ways to incorporate a variety of fruits, vegetables, and superfoods into your diet. Celebrate these achievements, no matter how small they may seem. Every glass of juice represents a choice you made for better health.

II. Overcoming Challenges and Staying Motivated

Along the way, you've likely faced challenges, from selecting the right equipment to finding the perfect balance of flavors in your juice recipes. Remember, every challenge encountered was an opportunity to learn and grow. You've adapted, experimented, and refined your techniques, gaining invaluable knowledge about juicing and nutrition.

Staying motivated can be tough, especially when life gets busy. It's important to remind yourself of why you started this journey. Was it to improve your energy levels? To support your family's health? Or perhaps to educate your clients on the benefits of juicing and holistic nutrition? Revisit these goals regularly to keep your passion for juicing alive.

III. Integrating Juicing into Your Daily Life

Now that juicing has become a part of your routine, think about ways to keep it exciting and integral to your daily life. This could mean experimenting with seasonal fruits and vegetables, exploring exotic juice recipes, or even growing your own produce for juicing. Embrace the joy of sharing your juice creations with friends and family, and take pride in the positive influence you're having on their health and wellness.

As you move forward, remember that your juicing journey doesn't have a final destination. It's a continuous path of discovery, learning, and enjoyment. Keep exploring new recipes, techniques, and ingredients. Stay curious and open to new possibilities. Your journey with juicing is as much about the process as it is about the delicious, healthful beverages you create.

Your journey with juicing has been a transformative experience, offering benefits that extend far beyond the glass. It's about embracing a lifestyle that prioritizes health, wellness, and the joy of discovering new tastes and nutrients. As you continue on this path, keep nurturing your body, mind, and soul with each refreshing sip. Here's to your health, vitality, and the endless possibilities that lie ahead in your juicing adventure.

Incorporating Juicing into Your Daily Routine

Embracing juicing as part of your daily life is a journey that evolves and adapts to your lifestyle, goals, and personal preferences. As we conclude this guide, let's explore how you can seamlessly integrate juicing into your everyday routine, enhancing both your health and that of your family. Remember, the key to successful juicing lies in making it a sustainable and enjoyable part of your life.

I. Establishing a Juicing Routine

Consistency is crucial when incorporating any new habit into your life, and juicing is no exception. Start by setting a specific time each day for juicing, whether it's a morning ritual to kickstart your day or an evening activity to unwind. Align this with your daily schedule to ensure it feels less like a chore and more like a cherished part of your routine.

Creating a weekly juicing plan can also help you stay on track. Plan your recipes in advance, taking into account the seasonal availability of produce and your family's preferences. This not only saves time but also ensures variety in your diet, keeping your juicing experience fresh and exciting.

II. Making Juicing a Family Affair

Involving your family in the juicing process can transform it from a solitary task to an engaging, educational, and fun activity. Teach your children about the benefits of different fruits and vegetables, and let them pick the ingredients for your next juice blend. This not only cultivates healthy eating habits but also strengthens your bond as a family.

Encourage family members to share their favorite recipes or create new ones together. This collaboration not only diversifies your juice menu but also makes the experience more enjoyable for everyone involved. Remember, the goal is to make juicing an integral and enjoyable part of your family's lifestyle.

III. Juicing as a Tool for Holistic Nutrition Education

Your journey with juicing provides a unique opportunity to educate yourself and your clients about holistic nutrition. Use your knowledge and experience to guide others in understanding how juicing complements a balanced diet. Share the science behind juicing, its health benefits, and how it can be tailored to meet individual nutritional needs.

Organize workshops or create informational content that covers various aspects of juicing, from selecting the right equipment to understanding the nutritional value of different ingredients. By educating others, you not only reinforce your own knowledge but also empower your community to make informed health choices.

Incorporating juicing into your daily routine is a rewarding endeavour that offers numerous health benefits. It's a commitment to yourself and your family, fostering a culture of wellness and mindful nutrition. As you move forward, let juicing be a source of health, joy, and creativity in your life. Embrace the endless possibilities it brings and let it guide you on your continuous path to wellness. Remember, every glass of juice is a step towards a healthier, happier you.

Continuing Your Path to Wellness

As we reach the conclusion of our journey through the world of juicing, it's time to reflect on how this practice can be a lifelong companion in your pursuit of wellness. Juicing is not just a fad or a temporary fix; it's a transformative lifestyle choice that can continually nurture your body and soul. Let's delve into how you can sustain this journey, enriching your life and those around you.

I. Embracing Juicing as a Lifelong Practice

Juicing is more than just a dietary choice; it's a commitment to nurturing your health with every sip. As you move forward, consider juicing an integral part of your daily nutrition. Regularly experimenting with new recipes and ingredients keeps your juicing routine vibrant and exciting. Stay open to learning and adapting – whether it's about new juicing techniques, the latest nutritional research, or seasonal produce offerings. Remember, the key to making juicing a lifelong habit is to keep it enjoyable and varied.

II. Nurturing Family Health and Bonding

Your juicing journey has the potential to positively impact not just your life but also the lives of your loved ones. Encourage your family to join in on the juicing fun. Make it a collaborative effort – from picking fresh produce at the farmers' market to experimenting with new recipes in the kitchen.

This shared experience can become a cherished family ritual, fostering stronger bonds and promoting a collective commitment to health.

For children, introduce juicing in a fun and interactive way. Let them press the juicer button or choose the fruits and vegetables. For the elderly, consider gentle, easy-to-digest juices that cater to their nutritional needs. Juicing can be a great way to ensure your family, regardless of age, receives their daily dose of vitamins and minerals.

III. Spreading the Word Through Education and Advocacy

As you grow more confident and knowledgeable in your juicing journey, consider sharing your experiences with others. You can become an advocate for healthy living in your community. Host juicing workshops, write a blog, or simply share recipes on social media. Educate others about the benefits of juicing and how it can be part of a balanced, holistic diet.

Remember, each story you share has the power to inspire someone else to start their own journey towards better health. Your journey can motivate others, creating a ripple effect of health and wellness.

In conclusion, your journey with juicing is a continuous path towards wellness, not a destination. It's about making conscious choices every day that honor and nourish your body. By embracing juicing as a lifelong practice, nurturing family health, and spreading the word through education and advocacy, you're not just drinking juice; you're imbibing a culture of health and vitality. Continue this journey with passion, curiosity, and joy, and watch as it positively transforms every facet of your life. Remember, in the world of juicing, every day is a new opportunity to nourish and flourish.

UPDATED 2025 edition with added contents

Dear reader,

Thank you for choosing to purchase ' Juicing for beginners'.

To express my gratitude, as an updated 2025 edition, I decided to offer you 3 exclusive gifts, two of which are related to my professional research:

1 - Juicing: mastering glycemic index
2 -The strategy of colors in Juices
3- Smoothie sensations as delicious recipes for a refreshing boost

I hope you enjoy these topics for their quality and the fun of your juicing needs.

To access your free and exclusive gift, simply scan the QR code shown here:

 **Juicing: mastering glycemic index**

 **The strategy of colors in Juices**

 **Smoothie sensations as delicious recipes for a refreshing boost**

Made in the USA
Monee, IL
15 December 2024

73906615R00057